ENDOCRINES
IN
DEVELOPMENT

The Developmental Biology Conference Series, 1956

HELD UNDER THE AUSPICES OF

THE NATIONAL ACADEMY OF SCIENCES
NATIONAL RESEARCH COUNCIL

Paul Weiss

ORGANIZER AND GENERAL CHAIRMAN

THE CONFERENCES

EMBRYONIC NUTRITION
Brown University, July 23–24
Chairman: J. S. NICHOLAS; *Reporter and editor:* DOROTHEA RUDNICK

REGENERATION IN VERTEBRATES
Brown University, July 23–24
Chairman: E. G. BUTLER; *Reporter and editor:* CHARLES S. THORNTON

CYTODIFFERENTIATION
Brown University, July 27–31
Chairmen: ERNST HADORN, HOLGER HYDÉN, W. E. ANKEL, V. B. WIGGLESWORTH,
and ISAAC BERENBLUM; *Reporter and editor:* DOROTHEA RUDNICK

ENVIRONMENTAL INFLUENCES ON PRENATAL DEVELOPMENT
Jackson Memorial Laboratory, August 2–4
Chairman: MEREDITH N. RUNNER; *Reporter and editor:* BEATRICE MINTZ

IMMUNOLOGY AND DEVELOPMENT
Jackson Memorial Laboratory, August 7–9
Chairman: JAMES D. EBERT; *Reporter and editor:* MAC V. EDDS, JR.

PHYSIOLOGY OF INSECT DEVELOPMENT
Macdonald College, August 14–16
Chairman: MAX F. DAY; *Reporter and editor:* FRANK L. CAMPBELL

DYNAMICS OF PROLIFERATING TISSUES
Brookhaven National Laboratory, September 5–8
Chairman: C. P. LEBLOND; *Reporter and editor:* DOROTHY PRICE

ENDOCRINES IN DEVELOPMENT
Shelter Island, N.Y., September 11–13
Chairman: B. H. WILLIER; *Reporter and editor:* RAY L. WATTERSON

MITOGENESIS
Argonne National Laboratory, September 24–26
Chairman: AUSTIN M. BRUES; *Reporters and editors:* H. S. DUCOFF *and* C. F. EHRET

WOUND HEALING AND TISSUE REPAIR
Rockefeller Institute, October 2–4
Chairman: FRANCIS D. MOORE; *Reporter and editor:* W. BRADFORD PATTERSON

ENDOCRINES
IN DEVELOPMENT

Edited by

RAY L. WATTERSON

THE UNIVERSITY OF CHICAGO PRESS

THE UNIVERSITY OF CHICAGO COMMITTEE
ON PUBLICATIONS IN BIOLOGY AND MEDICINE

The Library of Congress Catalog Card

⌐   ⌐

SYMPOSIUM ON ENDOCRINES IN DEVELOPMENT,
Shelter Island, N.Y., 1956.

   Endocrines in development, edited by Ray L.
Watterson. [Chicago] University of Chicago Press
[1959]

    xiii, 142 p. illus., diagrs. 24 cm. (The Develop-
mental biology conference series, 1956)

   Bibliography: p. 130–141.

   1. Endocrinology. I. Watterson, Ray Leighton, 1915–
ed. II. Title.   (Series)

QP187.S94 1956   611.4   59–8868

Library of Congress

L   ⌐

THE UNIVERSITY OF CHICAGO PRESS, CHICAGO 37
Cambridge University Press, London, N.W. 1, England
The University of Toronto Press, Toronto 5, Canada

© *1959 by The University of Chicago. Published 1959*
Composed and printed by THE UNIVERSITY OF CHICAGO PRESS
Chicago, Illinois, U.S.A.

Preface to the Series

Development and growth have usually been studied rather piecemeal: as embryology, or plant physiology, or nutrition, or oncology; as seriation of stages of chick embryos, as cell division in fish eggs or plant root tips, as growth curves of children, as hormone response of plumage, as spread of a fungus, as repair of a broken bone or the swelling of a diseased spleen; by observation, measurement, comparison, chemical alteration, excision, transplantation, or sheer speculation. Yet, in reality, all of these are merely isolated aspects of one broad continuous spectrum of phenomena; varied manifestations of the same basic principles and elementary processes: multiplication of organic mass (growth); diversification of that mass (differentiation); pattern formation (morphogenesis); progressive change (maturation and aging); and the repair or reproduction of patterns after disturbance (regulation and regeneration).

This unity of subject matter has received renewed emphasis in the "Developmental Biology Conference Series of 1956," a record of which is now presented in ten volumes, including the present report. The series consisted of co-ordinated and interdisciplinary conferences, symposia, and workshops, organized under the sponsorship of the Biology Council of the Division of Biology and Agriculture, National Academy of Sciences–National Research Council, with the generous financial support of governmental agencies, industrial organizations, and private foundations and donors (see list at end of Preface).

The Conference Series brought together experts from the fields of anatomy, biochemistry, biometry, biophysics, botany, cytology, embryology, endocrinology, genetics, histology, immunology, microbiology, neurology, nutrition, oncology, pathology, physiology, radiology, and zoölogy, from the United States and abroad, less for a display of most recent technical advances than for a concerted examination and evaluation of the contributions of these various specialties to the elucidation of focal issues of developmental biology. Fresh orientation and new ideas could be expected to emerge from this pool of critically distilled knowledge by the intersection of formerly unrelated trends of thought or by the discovery of common cores in formerly unrelated sets of data. Nearly three hundred

American and fifty-four foreign scientists (from nineteen countries) joined in this task.

To serve the outlined objective, the meetings had to be ruled by the key words: *perspective* and *relevance*. All participants were admonished to present only such itemized information, conclusions, demonstrations, criticisms, illustrations, questions, and quotations as promised to throw light on the *issue* under discussion; that is, to confine themselves to comments of "strategic" or "catalytic" pertinence, not merely adding to the bulk of information, but contributing to clarification, order, harmonization, and comprehensibility. Pertinent comments, however, were welcomed regardless of whether they referred to data so new as to be still largely unknown; so old as to have been widely forgotten; so specialized or technical as to have received limited currency among "outsiders"; so theoretical as to have escaped the practitioners; or so "self-evident" as to have evaded critical scrutiny. Each participant was expected to draw from his store of special knowledge points that might help correct misinterpretations, indicate the feasibility of new approaches, and, above all, reveal existing gaps of knowledge and understanding.

It is evident that a group exercise of this complexion, with free give-and-take, could not possibly "cover the ground" in any of the selected topics within the given time limits and without sacrificing spontaneity, informality, and depth of penetration. Often a few key issues, profoundly analyzed and critically elucidated, proved far more enlightening than a hurried bird's-eye view of a large field. In cases in which workers from different disciplines were only vaguely acquainted with one another's stock-in-trade and vocabulary, the time and effort spent describing even elementary facts in order to provide a common ground for communication proved very worthwhile indeed. In other instances, where the facts were familiar but their interpretation was controversial, it seemed preferable to let argumentation take precedence over the recital of facts.

The foregoing remarks are intended to explain the discursive nature of these volumes. In conferences which combine basic and clinical interests, technical and theoretical approaches, molecular and organismic concepts, botanical and zoölogical subjects, biochemical and morphological aspects, it is imperative to place the reconciliation and synthesis of viewpoints above all other considerations.

In line with this general precept, each conference chairman was to open his meeting with a brief keynote address, staking out the major problems for discussion. By phrasing questions, rather than stating theses, he was to set the stage for free, though not necessarily unpremeditated, participation. Most of the conferences were closed meetings, with attendance confined to the invited panel members. In a few cases, auditors were admitted. Only the symposia at Brown University, which were co-sponsored by the International Union of Biological Sciences, were open to the general public.

For the purpose of publication, an experienced scientist familiar with the subject matter was appointed as official reporter and editor for each conference, to attend all sessions without taking part in the discussions. From the sound-tape recordings of the proceedings and his or her own notes, each editor then produced a condensed version of the conference. These accounts constitute the substance of this series of publications.

The individual reports vary greatly in form, depending on the topic and organization of each conference, as well as on the personal predilections of the editor. Only in one instance has the dialogue style been kept, and even so, only after considerable pruning. In other cases, an entire conference has been reported as a third-person account, reordering the text rather liberally into a logical sequence by combining related fragments; in this process of synthesis, an editor assumed the full prerogatives of an author. Most of the reports, however, range somewhere between these two extremes, abstracting the major comments of the various participants without obliterating their identity, yet resorting to verbal quotations infrequently or not at all. Some participants furnished their own rewritten versions of the factual presentations, and these were in most cases inserted in the text as such. In all cases, the participants were given an opportunity to check their respective contributions, either in the original transcript or later in the condensed and revised text.

The lack of uniformity reflects the informal spirit of the meetings and accents the main theme of the Conference Series: that developmental biology is currently in a state of flux, fitting no rigid mold and shaping its own course as it gains momentum by the growth and confluence of its many tributaries. It is hoped that the publication of this series will add to that momentum, as did the conferences themselves.

To each of the participants but, above all, to the chairmen and editors, we owe a deep debt of gratitude. To the following donors of funds, we reiterate our appreciation for generous assistance: Atomic Energy Commission, U.S. Departments of the Air Force, Army, and Navy (Medical Services); Office of Naval Research; Fulbright Fellowship Program; National Institutes of Health; National Science Foundation; International Union of Biological Sciences; American Cyanamid Company; Diamond Alkali Company; Merck and Company, Inc.; Chas. Pfizer and Company,

Inc.; Rohm and Haas Company; E. R. Squibb and Sons; American Cancer Society; and Rockefeller Foundation. Special thanks are due to Dr. Russell B. Stevens, executive secretary of the Biology Council, for carrying the major load in the recording of the conferences; and to Mrs. Geraldine A. Norton, administrative assistant, for her effective help with the preparations and practical details of the meetings.

PAUL WEISS

NEW YORK CITY
May 1958

Endocrines in Development

HELD SEPTEMBER 11–13, 1956

AT

SHELTER ISLAND, NEW YORK

Conference chairman
B. H. WILLIER
Johns Hopkins University
Baltimore, Maryland

Reporter and editor
RAY L. WATTERSON
Northwestern University
Evanston, Illinois

Participants:

ROBERT K. BURNS, *Carnegie Institution of Washington, Baltimore, Maryland*

P. J. GAILLARD, *State University of Leiden, Leiden, Holland*

J. S. KOLLROS, *State University of Iowa, Iowa City, Iowa*

JAN LANGMAN, *Free University of Amsterdam, Amsterdam, Holland*

PETAR MARTINOVITCH, *Institute for Nuclear Science, Belgrade, Jugoslavia*

FLORENCE MOOG, *Washington University, St. Louis, Missouri*

O. MÜHLBOCK, *Institute for Cancer Research, Amsterdam, Holland*

DOROTHY PRICE, *University of Chicago, Chicago, Illinois*

HOWARD SCHNEIDERMAN, *Cornell University, Ithaca, New York*

O. E. SCHOTTÉ, *Amherst College, Amherst, Massachusetts*

SHELDON SEGAL, *Rockefeller Institute for Medical Research, New York, New York*

EMIL TONUTTI, *Medical Academy, Giessen, Germany*

PAUL WEISS, *Rockefeller Institute for Medical Research, New York, New York*

Contents

List of Illustrations

· I ·

Introduction

The conference was called to order by DR. WEISS, who emphasized that the sessions would deal with various aspects of the relation between endocrines and development. He pointed out that this is a two-way street. Endocrine glands undergo development, and, as they develop, they influence other organs, including other endocrine glands. Development may be considered in a broad sense as the large tidal wave of change that leads from conception to death, not broken up by the ripples of cyclic physiologic activities. Viewed in this light, the study of endocrines in development extends beyond the embryonic period into later stages, including maturation, puberty, metamorphosis, regeneration, pathologic changes, and metaplasia. Weiss introduced DR. WILLIER, chairman of the conference, who immediately reviewed the history and the highlights of the subject under discussion.

DR. WILLIER stated that he began his graduate work at a time when endocrinology was in its infancy. He first encountered the term "hormone" as a student of A. J. Carlson and F. R. Lillie at the University of Chicago. He participated in the analysis of the freemartin effect. He noted that the goal of the present conference is to exchange knowledge and understanding of the role of endocrines in the ontogenetic process. He suggested that the subject under discussion should be called "Genetic Endocrinology." Weiss (1950) coined the title "Genetic Neurology" for a conference devoted to problems of development, growth, and regeneration of the nervous system. Genetic endocrinology might be, to paraphrase Dr. Weiss, a discipline encompassing all those processes that lead up to the mature state of the endocrine system. Key issues concerning the part that hormones play in the ontogenetic process should be presented. These should be analyzed and elucidated critically from new angles. Gaps in knowledge and understanding should be emphasized. An attempt should be made to develop a common scheme or generalization into which seemingly unrelated facts can be fitted. New ideas should be engendered. Every effort should be made to evolve a

1

coherent and consistent picture of the role of the hormones in the growth and development of the organism.

Genetic endocrinology is a relatively young science, dating back to the investigations of Gudernatsch in 1912 and Adler in 1914. The work of Gudernatsch demonstrated that feeding thyroid to frog tadpoles initiates precocious metamorphosis within a few days. Two years later Adler reported in his significant paper that destruction of the anterior pituitary in frog tadpoles results in profound changes in the thyroid gland (growth retardation, production of a small amount of abnormal colloid, etc.) and likewise in the failure of the tadpoles to undergo metamorphosis. These pioneer investigations, although lacking in finish and polish, nevertheless opened the field to more critical and refined modes of exploration of the role of hormones in development. Progress was relatively slow in this subject for four decades. Within this period there are certain highlights in the history of developmental endocrinology, a few of which follow.

1. The functional relationships between the anterior pituitary, the thyroid, the adrenals, and the gonads are established during the course of development of the embryo. At first, the *functional dependence* of the various glands was stressed. Thus it was realized that the thyroid is dependent upon the anterior pituitary in some way. Gradually, the concept of the *functional interdependence* of the various glands emerged, an interdependence of anterior pituitary and thyroid, of anterior pituitary and adrenal. It is curious that the emphasis was placed at first upon the thyroid-pituitary relation rather than upon the adrenal-pituitary relation because Smith (1920) showed that when he removed the pituitary from tadpoles, the adrenal as well as the thyroid is affected.

2. Sex hormones act during the embryonic development of sex organs. This was demonstrated by the studies of Lillie (1916, 1917) on the freemartin. One facet of this analysis constituted part of Willier's doctoral thesis. Everyone is familiar with the impact that this discovery had upon investigations of the role of sex hormones in sex differentiation.

3. The endocrine receptor, or end organ, serves as a target for hormone action. The word "target" should always be used in quotes. The origin of this term is uncertain; it was probably laboratory jargon initially. There can be no target in the usual sense because a target is something that is shot at. Hormones are not shooting at anything; they are in circulation; they are picked up selectively. The terms "receptor" and "end organ" were borrowed from nerve physiology of the English school.

2

4. The receptor responds according to its intrinsic potentialities, which it acquires during the course of early development. The receptor develops reaction capacities before hormones are poured into the circulation. This concept is implied, but not specifically stated, in early papers. Lillie stated (1917, p. 419): "In the case of the free-martin we do not find that male hormones cause the development of any structure which is not represented embryologically in the normal female; the hormones act in this case merely by inhibition or stimulation of normal embryonic rudiments." The concept as we now understand it is clearly implied here. The following quotation is from a later paper by Lillie (1929, p. 521): "Goldschmidt also (1927) compares his 'organ forming substances' to hormones. So far as embryonic segregation, i.e. the origin of specific potencies, is concerned, the analogy is entirely inappropriate because, as I pointed out with reference to the sex-hormones (Lillie, 1927b), the action of hormones presupposes specific potency of the substrate. The hormone does not act by creation of segregates, but only by stimulation or inhibition of existing substrates." Clearly, the concept of selective response of the receptor is inherent in these statements quoted from Lillie's text.

5. Hormones act synergistically to produce their effects. This concept can be traced back to a paper of Smith (1933) or even earlier if one reads between the lines. Smith was the first to show that hormones produced by the anterior pituitary and by the thyroid have a synergistic action in promoting the growth of the rat. This concept has been confirmed by investigations at the University of California utilizing purified hormones such as thyroxin and growth hormone (Simpson, Asling, and Evans, 1950; Geschwind and Li, 1955). Thus an interlocking action of hormones is involved in regulating growth and development.

6. A reciprocal influence is established between endocrine glands. This has been emphasized by Moore and Price (1932). Their discovery is known to everyone working in this field and certainly deserves recognition here.

7. Vertebrate and insect hormones have been isolated, purified, and/or synthesized. First the synthesis of adrenalin should be mentioned and next the synthesis of thyroxin. Steroid hormones, both sex hormones and adrenocortical hormones, were synthesized later. Next should be mentioned the greatest triumph of all because it dealt with proteins, namely, the determination of the structure of three species of insulin molecules —those of cattle, sheep, and hogs—by Sanger and his collaborators in recent years (Sanger and Tuppy, 1951a, b; Sanger and Thompson, 1953a, b; Sanger, Smith, and Kitai, 1954). Almost equally remarkable

3

was the determination of the structure of hog beta corticotrophin by Bell in 1954 and by Howard *et al.* in 1955 and of sheep alpha cortico-trophin by Li *et al.*, of the University of California, in 1955. Almost si-multaneously appeared the work of Du Vigneaud (1956) and his asso-ciates on oxytocin and vasopressin, which are small peptide hormones of the posterior pituitary. Thus the constitution of many hormones is now well known. Yet how little is known about the crucial reactions which these hormones release in the terminal receptors! Discovery of the chemical constitution of hormones will surely have an impact on studies concerned with the mechanism of action of hormones on receptors. The receptor picks up the hormone molecule selectively, somewhat as a tele-vision set picks up frequencies selectively. There is some kind of match-ing between hormone molecules and something in the receptor. They fit together somehow, and knowledge of the chemical constitution of hor-mones may aid in understanding how hormones are picked up selec-tively and how hormones produce changes in receptors.

· II ·

Ontogeny of Selected Endocrine Glands:
The Thyroid

DR. WILLIER introduced the topic by outlining the development of the thyroid. This gland arises from the floor of the pharynx. A small bud is cut off, which becomes circular in outline. This circular body constricts into two by some process of morphogenesis which is not understood, resulting in formation of two circular bodies, one right and one left. Thus the thyroid epithelium exists in the form of two sacs. WEISS inquired whether any abnormality is known that affects this dichotomy. He called attention to the similarity of the dichotomy that occurs during lung development and stated that they were attempting, with some success, to block the latter experimentally. He emphasized that application of the classical methods of embryology to the problem of the factors involved in producing the dichotomy of the thyroid rudiment would probably be productive of results. BURNS remarked that he could recall no case where this dichotomy is completely arrested. He did point out that the finished organ is never completely subdivided; the two lobes remain more or less connected. He recalled that a median thyroid can persist in its own right, to give rise to a thyroid mass which may even be imbedded in the base of the tongue quite close to its original point of origin.

WILLIER continued by stating that this epithelium breaks up into a series of interlocking cords surrounded by a connective tissue capsule. Between these epithelial cords are large spaces, resembling sinusoids, filled with blood. This blood is received from a branch of the internal carotid artery (see Willier, 1955, Fig. 208). The sinusoids are especially conspicuous at the time when the interlacing cords begin to form follicles and colloid begins to appear in them. A critical stage in the development of the thyroid with respect to the formation of sinusoids and their association with follicles occurs between the tenth and eleventh days of incubation in the case of the chick.

Willier's use of the term "epithelial cords" was questioned by GAIL-

LARD. He inquired whether individual thyroid cells could actually be distinguished from one another. In his work on thyroid development he never sees any sign of borders between cells at this time; he sees only syncytial or symplasmic cords containing many nuclei. Cell boundaries appear quite suddenly a little later. In response to these questions, WILLIER asked whether it was not true that the cell surface was not very well defined in many animal tissues, particularly during embryonic development. GAILLARD then commented on his observations on thyroid development as follows:

In thyroid glands cultured in the absence of the anterior pituitary and thus in the absence of anterior pituitary hormones, unless the latter are present in very low concentration in the human or cock plasma which is used, colloid droplets always arise quite close to the nuclei, juxtanuclear, within symplasmic cords. In the chick embryo the droplets can be found at any place in the thyroid gland in between nuclei. When the thyroid gland from an 8-day chick embryo is cultivated, further development of the tissue structure occurs rather slowly. This means that the symplasmic stage sometimes last for 2 or 3 days. During this period hundreds of small colloid droplets develop in close relation to the nuclei; they then increase in volume and sometimes push aside neighboring nuclei. Gradually a number of nuclei become arranged around a big colloid droplet, and it is about this time that cell borders develop microscopically. Follicle development is retarded for 1 or 2 days. Follicle formation begins, but follicles with high columnar epithelium are never formed. All cells remain cuboidal. Even in the presence of TSH (thyroid-stimulating hormone), fully developed follicles never form in vitro, although an increased amount of colloid is observed. Colloid formation and the arrangement of cells into follicles are therefore to be considered as dissociable processes. The cords mentioned by Willier do not often develop during cultivation in vitro, although they are seen occasionally in glands cultivated in the presence of TSH. In these cases the spaces between the cords resemble sinuses; they are filled with a substance which is slightly eosinophilic and with some erythrocytes and mononucleate cells.

WILLIER stated that some development independent of stimulation from some other endocrine gland is a characteristic feature of all endocrine glands but that development will continue only to a certain point in the absence of such stimulation. BURNS said that this is certainly true in completely hypophysectomized amphibian larvae. Even rudimentary follicles may be present as well as small amounts of colloid (Smith, 1920). Then development stops without further stimulation.

This would argue against the presence of any thyrotrophic hormone in the plasma of the clot.

WEISS then inquired whether mitotic division occurs without concurrent division of the cytoplasm. GAILLARD answered in the affirmative. WEISS then called attention to the fact that there had long been a suspicion that the neural tube was a syncytial organ but that more penetrating analyses (Sauer, 1935*a, b;* Watterson *et al.,* 1956) revealed it to be truly cellular. Cell boundaries are simply very difficult to see. He also remarked that the electron microscope reveals cell boundaries in embryonic stages where they were thought to be lacking. He questioned whether it is certain that distinct cells are lacking in thyroids of embryos. GAILLARD answered that they cannot be seen at first with the highest magnification of the light microscope, even if the preparations are stained with Hellblau, which usually reveals cell boundaries very nicely. One or 2 days later they can be seen. WEISS commented that he was emphasizing this point because an extremely interesting principle of morphogenesis would be involved. This would be one of the few cases of a nucleated tube growing out into a linear structure similar to the hyphae of fungi. Weiss considered the problem to be worthy of further investigation.

WILLIER continued by stating that there is considerable evidence that the primordium of the thyroid can pick up radioactive iodine selectively before there are any follicles, indicating that specific cell strains are already involved. In other words, the cells are already fixed as specifically thyroid cells. He called attention to a recent paper, the reference to which he could not recall, where someone had introduced radioactive iodine into a human mother, following which the thyroid of the embryo had picked up the radioactive iodine selectively. In this case it had gone through the placenta. GAILLARD mentioned that he had some radio-autographs showing the addition of one-eightieth of a millicurie of I^{131} to cultures; selective absorption of I^{131} occurs approximately 1 day before the first sign of colloid formation occurs in vitro, i.e., before the colloid can be distinguished histologically.

WEISS then inquired about the thyroid tissue which grows out from the explant in vitro. He was thinking of the work of Carpenter (1942) and others. He asked whether distinct cells were visible in the epithelial outgrowth. GAILLARD answered that she had cultivated whole organs and had not obtained an epithelial outgrowth. However, Demuth (1933) and Ebeling (1924) grew fragments of older thyroid glands on cover glasses years ago and obtained epithelial membranes with well-bordered cells.

WEISS asked to what extent it is possible to dissociate the effect of TSH on differentiation or rate of development of the gland from its effect on the production of a product, namely, colloid. GAILLARD answered that TSH causes only increased production of colloid and has no effect on the development of thyroid structure. WILLIER commented that in the experiments of Fugo (1940), who hypophysectomized chick embryos by extirpation of the forebrain, the development of the thyroid is slowed by the eleventh day of incubation, suggesting that the speed of development is reduced in the absence of thyrotrophic hormone. GAILLARD stated that Fugo's results caused him to expect that TSH would have an influence on the formation of follicles when added to his thyroid cultures, but there is no such effect. WEISS then inquired whether TSH has any action on the discharge of colloid from thyroid cells. GAILLARD called attention to the experiments of Gonzales (1956), who found that thyroxin, mono-, and diiodotyrosine, as well as some unknown iodine-labeled products, are present in explanted thyroids but not in the culture medium. Such experiments indicated that no discharge of the products had occurred. By contrast, corticosteroids produced by explants of the adrenal cortex of young rats are released into the culture medium. MARTINOVITCH questioned the results obtained by Gonzales. He stated that Pavlović, Roche, and Michel were studying the function of explanted thyroid glands of infantile rats with the aid of I^{131}, electrophoresis, and paper chromatography and that they could demonstrate the presence of mono- and diiodotyrosine in the culture medium.

WEISS then presented a general scheme of problematic interactions and feedback mechanisms that should be kept in mind in an analysis of any relationships as complex as those between the pituitary and the thyroid (Fig. 1). The growth and differentiation of the pituitary gland lead to formation of a product (TSH), which is then discharged. The discharged TSH acts on a structure in the process of growth and differentiation, namely, the thyroid gland. The latter structure, in turn, is producing certain products, one of which is thyroxin, which may or may not be discharged. Does TSH affect growth of the thyroid gland (Fig. 1, arrow *1*), differentiation of the thyroid (arrow *2*), formation of the product of the thyroid (arrow *3*), or discharge of the product (arrow *4*)? Does the product of the thyroid affect growth (arrow *5*) and/or differentiation (arrow *6*) of the thyroid while it is still inside the thyroid gland, or does it affect growth (arrow *7*) and/or differentiation (arrow *8*) of the thyroid cells only after it is discharged from the thyroid? Does the discharged product of the thyroid gland also affect the

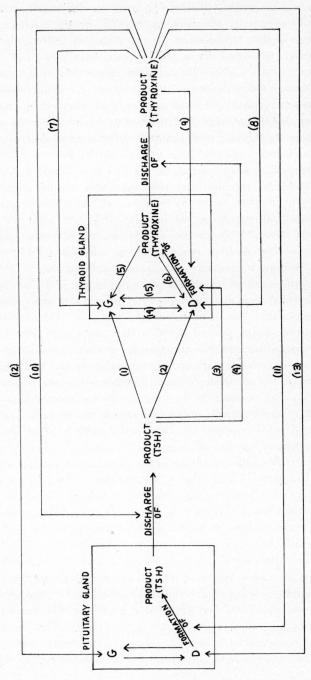

Fig. 1.—Problematic interactions and feedback mechanisms between the pituitary gland (source of trophic hormone TSH) and the thyroid gland (source of thyroxin). G = growth; D = differentiation. (Weiss original.)

production of the product (arrow *9*)? Does the discharged product of the thyroid affect only the discharge of TSH by the pituitary gland (arrow *10*), or does it also affect the production of TSH by the pituitary (arrow *11*)? Does discharged thyroxin have any effect on the growth (arrow *12*) and/or differentiation (arrow *13*) of the pituitary gland? Perhaps within the thyroid there is some sort of antagonistic relation between growth and differentiation such that, when growth is stimulated, differentiation is inhibited (arrow *14*) or vice versa (arrow *15*). Perhaps the mere act of discharge of the thyroid product stimulates the thyroid gland to produce and/or to accumulate more of its product. Such a diagram serves to emphasize the fact that merely stating that TSH produced by the pituitary gland stimulates thyroid activity and that thyroxin produced by the thyroid gland inhibits pituitary activity is an oversimplification of the actual situation.

TONUTTI recalled that Rawson and Money (1949) were concerned with some of the questions raised by Weiss and stated that Fabbrini (1955a), working in his laboratory, studied the influence of thyroxin and triiodothyronine on the growth-promoting action of a given amount of TSH on the thyroid gland of hypophysectomized rats where no release of TSH is possible. The growth-promoting action of TSH was found to be diminished. SEGAL pointed out that the administration of a given hormone causes hypofunction and atrophy of the corresponding endocrine gland. It certainly does not cause growth of the gland that normally secretes the administered hormone. This is true for thyroxin administration and its effect on the thyroid, sex hormone administration and its effect on the gonads, or corticoid administration and its effect on the adrenals. This principle also holds when there is an imbalance in the production of endogenous hormones. In cases of hyperfunction of the adrenal cortex with an overproduction of adrenal androgens, gonadal hypofunction results. Segal believes that the possibility that a hormone can exert an effect on the organ producing it still remains open.

MOOG stated that it has been shown experimentally that administration of cortisone causes no additional reduction in the size of the adrenals of hypophysectomized rats. SEGAL agreed but pointed out that, by that time, the adrenals are down to the minimal size, which is independent of the trophic action of ACTH. He suggested that before this minimal level is reached, the direct action of a steroid hormone on the adrenal cortex must still be considered a possibility. For example, the direct inhibitory influence of steroids on one or the other component of the embryonic gonad is clearly shown by experiments involving administration of steroids to amphibian larvae; sex reversal is the consequence. This occurs in the presence or in the absence of the hypophysis (Chang and Witschi, 1955a). TONUTTI mentioned that in their unpublished studies of nuclear size in the adrenal cortex of hypophysectomized animals they found no additional decrease in size after administration of cortisone.

WILLIER then called attention to experiments carried out by one of his former students (Dossel, 1954, 1957), who isolated the thyroid sac of chick embryos and transplanted it to some other location on the body of another embryo. In certain experiments it was placed in the head close to the host pituitary; in other experiments it was placed posteriorly, near the base of the allantoic stalk. When transplanted to the head, together with its surrounding mesenchyme, it forms a mass of typical thyroid tissue. But if the thyroid sac is transplanted free from its surrounding mesenchyme (removed either by enzyme treatment or by dissection), no growth of the graft occurs. Thus the local mesenchyme of the thyroid rudiment seems to have a highly specific action; foreign mesenchyme of the head will not substitute for it in such a way as to enable the thyroid rudiment to undergo further development. Similarly, the foreign mesenchyme of the tail cannot substitute for the specific mesenchyme of the thyroid gland. Thus the mesenchyme of the thyroid gland appears to play an important role in the development of the thyroid, but the nature of this role remains unknown. GAILLARD recalled the very similar role of specific mesenchyme in the development of other structures, as demonstrated by Grobstein (1953). BURNS mentioned that the particular mesenchyme in the vicinity of the bulbo-urethral glands can be recognized before the gland itself has developed very far. A large area of condensation appears in the mesenchyme lateral to the urogenital sinus at the point where the bulbo-urethral gland is to appear. The gland itself is represented, at this time, by a small bud on the surface of the sinus. Probably the mesenchymal capsule of other glands plays a much more significant role in their development than has previously been recognized. WEISS reminded the conference that he had long been an advocate of the notion of differentiation of the mesenchyme. If the pre-mesenchyme of the limb bud is isolated and is dissociated into its individual cells, which are allowed to reaggregate at random in vitro, cartilage of the limb type is formed. If the mesenchyme around the eye is similarly isolated and dissociated into individual cells before there is any cartilage or pre-cartilage, a plate of sclera cartilage forms following their reaggregation in vitro, and this type of cartilage is quite different from that

11

of a limb. Thus the mesenchyme is clearly differentiating in each case in accordance with the organ territory from which it is taken.

WILLIER then called attention to still another striking example of the differentiation of the mesenchyme provided by Cairns and Saunders (1954). A piece of mesenchyme taken from the prospective thigh region of a leg bud of a chick embryo and placed in the prospective shoulder region of a wing bud induces formation of thigh-type feathers on the wing. Thus the mesenchyme of the leg bud is already specified at the time of transplantation, not only as leg mesoderm but as mesoderm of a specific region of the leg. He suggested that there is a great diversity of problems which could be analyzed to determine the role of specific mesenchyme in the development of endocrine glands and endocrine receptors.

SEGAL added still another example of this phenomenon. In the development of the adrenal of selachians, Chieffi (1952) described a mass of cells that he believed to represent a proliferation of the coelomic epithelium or of the dorsal root of the mesentery. These cells give rise to the adrenal cortex. They could just as well be interpreted as a condensation of the mesenchymal tissue in this region. Thus they could be interpreted as a specific part of the mesenchyme which plays an important role in the development of one of the endocrine glands. WEISS stated that, actually, the entire mesodermal component of the limb bud of the tadpole comes from the coelomic epithelium. The peritoneum becomes loosened in a localized area, and cells migrate out to form the solid mass of mesenchyme which constitutes the mesodermal core of the limb bud (Taylor, 1943, 1944).

· III ·

Ontogeny of Selected Endocrine Glands:
The Adrenals

The development of a second endocrine gland, the adrenals, was then reviewed by DR. WILLIER. He recalled that this is a composite organ composed of cortex and medulla and that these two components have separate origins. The cortex arises from a series of cords that invaginate from the coelomic epithelium just anterior to the site of the embryonic gonads. The medullary or chromaffin cells arise from the sympathoblasts, which are capable of forming either sympathetic neurons or chromaffin cells. The sympathoblasts are presumably derivatives of the neural crest. Willier (1930) demonstrated that the cortex can arise quite independently of the sympathetic component. At least it is possible to obtain chorio-allantoic grafts composed of typical cortical cords in the complete absence of chromaffin cells. Such grafts are isolated originally from donors in the head-process stage. He stressed the fact that only those sympathoblasts which come into intimate contact with cortical cells give the chromaffin reaction; this reaction indicates the presence of adrenalin or noradrenalin, the precursor of adrenalin. He stated that the sympathoblasts of mammalian embryos migrate through the cortex as little nests of cells (Flint, 1900), which develop a characteristic vascular pattern resembling the glomeruli of the kidney (see Willier, 1955, FIG. 209, B). After onset of this migration the sympathoblasts not only show the chromaffin reaction but also react positively to physiologic tests for the presence of adrenalin. However, if contact of sympathoblasts with cortex is essential for the differentiation of these cells into medullary cells of the adrenal, it is difficult to understand why other sympathoblasts which do not make this contact are able to differentiate into the organs of Zuckerkandl, i.e., into the chromaffin bodies located up and down the vertebral column. These are known to contain adrenalin or noradrenalin, the latter predominating in the fetus, the former in the adult.

WILLIER also emphasized the specific nature of the circulatory pattern of the adrenals, which is present by the time the glands are known to be producing various cortisones. The development of the characteristic palisade structure of the adrenals is not dependent upon the development of this specific circulatory pattern. MARTINOVITCH showed a photomicrograph of a section of a cultured adrenal gland taken from an infantile rat; the typical palisade structure had developed in vitro in the absence of blood vessels. WEISS suggested that the palisading of the adrenal cells, as well as the special orientation of the capillaries, probably represents a response to some more basic structure of the ground substance, instead of one being the cause of the other. KOLLROS referred briefly to his work (1949), which showed that grafted heads of tadpoles develop an arrangement of the major blood vessels at the surface of the brain, as well as of the capillaries, which is quite different from normal brains. This would seem to imply that the basic structure of the ground substance of the brain is not the only factor involved in the development of specific vascular patterns. For example, there are fewer radially arranged penetrating vessels in the midbrain portion of the graft than in the corresponding region of control embryos.

TONUTTI inquired whether anyone participating in the conference was familiar with the so-called second proliferation of the adrenocortical tissue. In the human embryo the first proliferation from the coelomic epithelium forms the fetal cortex, whereas the second proliferation occurring after birth establishes the definitive adrenal cortex at the surface of the fetal cortex (Keene and Hewer, 1927; Uotila, 1940). This caused BURNS to comment on the parallel between the development of the adrenals and that of the gonads. They are located very close together in early stages of development, and they both show two generations of proliferation, resulting, in the case of the gonad, in the formation of two generations of sex cords. The development of these two structures becomes increasingly parallel, the more it is pursued.

WILLIER then called attention to the fact that Witschi (1956) presents a different account of the origin of the adrenals from the one given above. SEGAL presented Witschi's point of view and attempted to show that there is actually very little difference in the two interpretations. He referred to Figure 54 in Witschi's textbook, which shows the intermediate mesoderm of *Hyla crucifer* located between the somite mesoderm and the lateral mesoderm. The region of the lateral plate that will later become the splanchnic mesodermal plate is in direct contact with the intermediate mesoderm. If this relationship is kept in mind, it is clear that the question concerning the origin of the adrenal cortex is simply whether it arises from one or the other of the two mesodermal

14

areas, which are, in fact, continuous with each other if observed early enough in development. Witschi's Figure 85 (1956) shows a stage just after hatching in *Rana sylvatica* larvae; the lateral mesodermal plates have fused in the mid-line. The right and left cardinal veins are still lateral in position, but they now begin to migrate medially, to fuse ventral to the dorsal aorta to form the single caval vein. In doing so, the right and left cardinal veins cut beneath the intermediate meso- derm, separating the latter from the lateral mesoderm. The right and left masses of intermediate mesoderm then migrate medially until they fuse in the dorsal mid-line between the dorsal aorta and the newly formed caval vein, to form the first definitive adrenal mass. From this the right and left adrenals eventually start their ventrolateral migra- tion along the venous lacunae bordering on the mesonephric bodies (Witschi, 1956, Fig. 90). The cortical elements are then joined by sympathoblasts, which leave the sympathetic ganglia. These nests of sympathoblasts assume chromaffin characteristics as they leave the ganglia and give rise to the adrenal medulla. Thus there really is not much difference in the two views concerning the origin of the adrenal cortex. The one states that the cortical rudiment arises from the coe- lomic epithelium; the other that the cortical rudiment originates from the intermediate mesoderm. Both sources are actually continuous at earlier stages than those usually examined.

SEGAL called attention to one other point. The interpretation pre- sented above emphasizes that the adrenal cortex and the medullary component of the gonads actually have a common origin from the intermediate mesoderm. Hence the functional similarities between the two become reduced to an embryological basis. It thus becomes possible to speak of the steroid glands—the adrenal cortex and the gonadal medulla; both originate from a common primordium.

GAILLARD then commented on some unpublished observations of Dr. Schaberg made in his laboratory on the functional activity of adrenal glands of the 5-day rat grown in vitro. He cultivates the outer portion of the cortex with the adjacent connective tissue. After a few days the connective tissue capsule grows to surround the whole explant, and all spongiocyte-type cells disappear. Only a very regularly distributed glomerulosa-type cell develops. In confronted cultures where this type of adrenal cortical explant is combined with fresh anterior pituitary fragments taken from rats of the same age, fairly large, vacuolated cells develop inside the adrenal explant; these exhibit all the cytologic characteristics of the stimulated spongiocyte-type cell. But, if the an- terior hypophysis tissue is cultivated for 6 days prior to combining

15

fragments of this gland with the explants of adrenal cortex, it has no effect on the latter. Adrenal cortical explants cultivated in the presence of ACTH exhibit the same kind of changes as under the influence of fresh anterior pituitary tissue. In fact, Dr. Schaberg studied the effects of different concentrations of ACTH (from 10 IU/cc to 1/1,000,000 IU/cc). An optimal effect is obtained with 2 IU/cc to 1/50 IU/cc. Considering the fact that fresh anterior hypophysis explants and ACTH give analogous effects, it seems likely that the fresh hypophysis tissue releases ACTH into the culture medium.

In order to study the effect in more detail, it was decided not to try to estimate the amount of ACTH in the medium because this hormone is known to be a rather unstable compound in blood plasma at 37° C. Instead, it was decided to try to estimate the amount of corticosterone in the medium with the help of the Saffran test (Saffran and Schally, 1955). Transformation of glomerulosa cells into spongiocyte cells always coincides with an increased amount of corticosteroids in the medium. Conversely, no increase in corticosteroids is found when formation of spongiocytes does not occur.

As described above, precultivation of anterior hypophysis tissues leads to a loss of effect on adrenal explants. This lack of effect could be overcome by the addition of hypothalamic tissue taken from the region of the median eminence. This discovery reveals that the cultivated anterior hypophysis tissue is still capable of releasing ACTH but that it lacks some activator which normally originates in the hypothalamus. SCHNEIDERMAN inquired whether it was necessary to have cellular continuity between the hypothalamic tissue and the cultured pituitary in order to get this effect. GAILLARD stated that such continuity is not necessary. SCHNEIDERMAN pointed out that this is exceedingly interesting because, to his knowledge, there have been few demonstrations of an action of neurosecretory cells in this manner when they are separated from their normal end organs. GAILLARD commented that in the present experiments hypothalamus tissue and anterior hypophysis tissue are cultured in the same medium, but at a distance of about $\frac{1}{2}$ cm. from one another. Nevertheless, products originating from the hypothalamic tissue evidently reached the anterior hypophysis tissue. The latter reacted by producing and/or releasing ACTH, which, in turn, stimulated the glomerulosa cells to transform into spongiocytes, which produced and released ketosteroids into the medium. SCHNEIDERMAN then asked whether extracts of hypothalamic tissue can exert similar effects. GAILLARD replied that this type of analysis is under way. WEISS inquired whether hypothalamic cells establish connections with the anterior pituitaries in tissue culture via nerve fibers. GAILLARD answered that no such fiber connections are established in the cultures.

SCHNEIDERMAN then stated that, although neurosecretory substances are tremendously important in the co-ordination of endocrine activities, investigators have succeeded in getting isolated neurosecretory materials to work in only a few instances. For example, 50 silkworm brains can be ground up and extracted, and the extract can be tested for neuro-secretory activity in an appropriate insect test system. But there is no activity. However, if a single living brain is implanted into the same test system, tremendous neurosecretory activity is obtained. Only Guillemin (1957) and Guillemin *et al.* (1955, 1956) succeeded in get-ting active extracts from the various hypothalamic nuclei of mammals. TONUTTI mentioned that he had made such extracts and that he could also isolate active substances by chromatographic techniques. SCHNEI-DERMAN then inquired whether they are proteinaceous materials. TONUTTI answered that they are polypeptides. MOOG added that Saffran, Schally, and Benfey (1955) had some evidence that the corticotrophin-releasing factor is a peptide. WILLIER then asked whether the posterior pituitary has the same effect as the hypothalamus; he would expect this, since neurosecretory nerves from the hypothalamus terminate in the neural lobe of the pituitary. GAILLARD answered that this has not been tested.

MARTINOVITCH then pointed out that spongiocyte-like cells can ap-pear in cultures of rat adrenal glands in the absence of both the pituitary gland and ACTH. They either form as islands of cells in the mass of undifferentiated cortical tissue or are scattered through it individually or in pairs. Similar cells are found in adrenal glands of hypophysecto-mized-grafted rats and in the adrenals of animals which are incompletely hypophysectomized (Martinovitch, 1955).

WILLIER inquired whether Gaillard had made any histochemical or cytochemical tests on adrenal glands cultured in vitro. GAILLARD re-plied that spongiocytes give a positive reaction to Sudan black. WILLIER then asked whether the reactions are any different when the anterior pituitary is associated with the adrenals in vitro. GAILLARD answered that the typical reactions are found as soon as the spongiocytes have developed under the influence of the anterior hypophysis. SEGAL asked for a description of the normal adrenal gland at this stage. GAILLARD stated that they show a beautiful stratification, with a zona glomerulosa and a zona fasciculata. But, as soon as they are explanted, all fascicu-lata-type cells disappear. Most of them die. If fresh anterior pituitary, or ACTH, or cultured pituitary tissue plus hypothalamus is added to the adrenal cultures after the fasciculata cells have disappeared, this

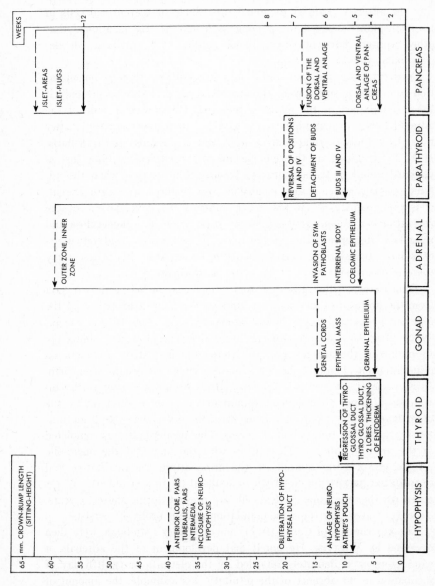

Fig. 2.—Diagram showing *formation of the anlage* of endocrine glands in relation to age and length of human embryos. Redrawn from Tonutti and Fetzer (1956).

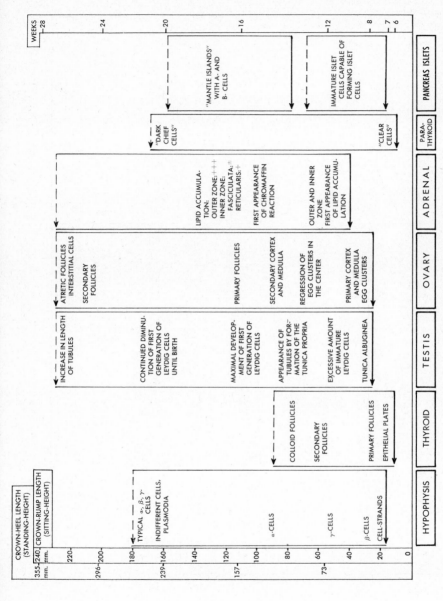

Fig. 3.—Diagram showing successive steps of *differentiation* of specific structural (and in part histochemical) constituents of endocrine glands in relation to age and length of human embryos. Redrawn from Tonutti and Fetzer (1956). Mantle islands are fetal islets with B cells in the center surrounded by a thick layer of A cells (Ferner, 1952).

21

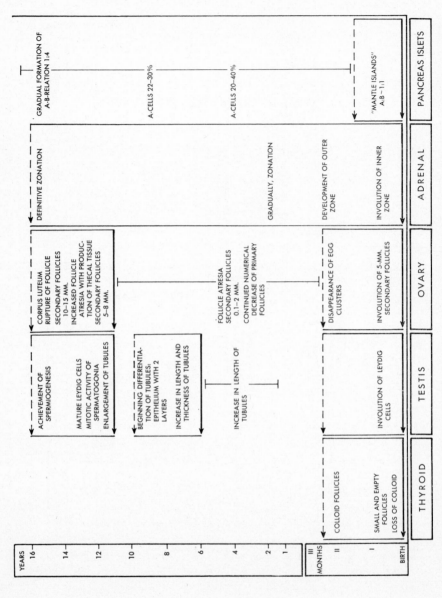

Fig. 4.—Changes in endocrine glands after birth and "maturation" of the structural elements of endocrine glands in relation to age up to puberty. Redrawn from Tonutti and Fetzer (1956).

WIESS inquired whether this reduction is for the whole gland or on a per cell basis. WILLIER informed him that it is for the whole gland. WEISS then asked whether the growth of the organ is reduced. WILLIER answered that the wet weights of pairs of adrenals are less than normal after the fifteenth day of incubation and fail to increase above the level attained by normal 15-day embryos. MOOG pointed out that the amount of ascorbic acid reported by Case is the total for the entire gland, medulla as well as cortex, as determined by the method of Roe and Kuether (1943), and that his results are expressed as so much ascorbic acid per milligram of adrenal tissue. Consequently, the concentration of ascorbic acid in the cortex itself remains unknown. WILLIER also mentioned Case's observations on the lipid content of the adrenals following hypophysectomy. The amount of lipid-containing cortical material is greatly diminished in partially decapitated embryos, at least by the eighteenth day of incubation. Whether it is diminished at earlier stages is not known. When ACTH is injected subcutaneously on the twelfth, fourteenth, and sixteenth days of incubation, larger amounts of lipid-containing cortical material are present by the eighteenth day of incubation, but the total amount is not equal to that of normal embryos. Despite the apparent increase in cortical elements after treatment with ACTH, there does not appear to be any increase in total size of the glands. These observations indicate that the adrenals of pituitaryless embryos can accumulate ascorbic acid and lipids to a limited extent but that they cannot accumulate them in the quantities characteristic of normal embryos. Thus it appears that the anterior pituitary plays some role in the further development of the adrenals by accelerating the rate of their development and the accumulation of these substances. This means, of course, that anterior pituitary hormones are released into the circulation of the embryo in effective amounts.

The discussion then turned to the work of Moog on the effects of ACTH on adrenal growth and adrenal secretion in the intact chick embryo (Moog and Ford, unpublished). An ACTH solution is injected into a vein on the chorio-allantois at daily intervals from 10 days on; the dose is 0.25 mg. of ACTH per day. The relative weights of the adrenals of treated embryos are consistently greater than those of the controls from 12 days on (Fig. 5). At 13 days the P-value of the mean difference between experimentals and controls is above 0.05, but for all other days the differences between experimentals and controls are highly significant. Although Case (1952) found that the adrenal weight in his partially decapitated embryos did not begin to fall behind that of the intact controls before 16 days, the present results demonstrate that the adrenals are able to respond to stimulation by exogenous ACTH well before that time. Although it is suspected that the stimulation affects only the cortex, no quantitative data are available concerning that point.

WEISS inquired about the drop in relative weights of the adrenals in control embryos at 15 days. MOOG replied that the matter is not very

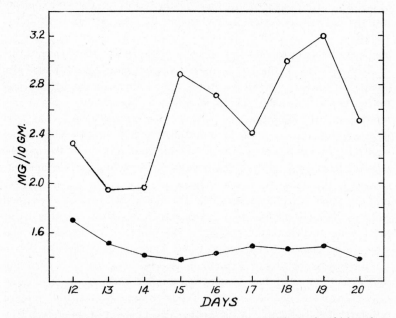

FIG. 5.—The influence of ACTH on relative adrenal weight in the chick embryo. *Open circles,* embryos injected intravenously with 0.25 mg. ACTH per day beginning at 10 days; *solid circles,* control embryos injected with acidified saline. The ordinate represents milligrams adrenal weight per 10 gm. of body weight. Absolute values of the adrenals of injected embryos were also higher than those of controls at each stage tested, but body weights were lower. (Moog, unpublished.)

clear. According to the data of Case (1952), relative adrenal weights do not change much during this period, but the data of Sun (1932) and Venzke (1943) likewise show a decrease in relative weights during the early incubation period, with a minimum at about 15 days. Both Case's data and those of Moog suggest that adrenal growth is controlled by a different set of factors before and after 15 days.

WILLIER inquired how cleanly the adrenal complex can be isolated. MOOG answered that it is not very difficult to isolate it after 15 days because it is sharply circumscribed at that time. But at earlier stages it is difficult to be certain that the whole gland is removed and nothing else. WEISS expressed his concern about the effect of ACTH injections on body weight. MOOG stated that the body is somewhat smaller than normal from 15 days on. WEISS then commented that anything that depressed the growth of the rest of the embryo would, of course, raise the values for relative weights of the adrenals even if there is no effect on the adrenals. MOOG agreed but pointed out that the percentage differences in adrenal weights are considerably greater than those in body weights. WEISS then asked whether the absolute weights of the adrenals are slightly elevated or slightly depressed. MOOG answered that they are strongly elevated. At 15 days, for example, the adrenals of injected embryos are twice as heavy as those of controls, and the difference is highly significant. She also mentioned that ACTH elevates liver glycogen but stated that the mechanism of its action is not clear. It also causes an enlargement of the spleen, for reasons which are not understood. Both these effects are apparent by 13 days, i.e., at a time when the effect on the absolute weight of the adrenal itself is not clearly significant. WILLIER then recalled that Case (1952) had reported that the spleen was greatly enlarged in hypophysectomized chick embryos.

MOOG then presented evidence of heightened secretion from adrenals stimulated by ACTH injections. The test she uses for secretion from the adrenals involves the increase in phosphatase in the duodenum, where, of course, the enzyme is extremely concentrated. Duodenal phosphatase in the mouse increases about a thousand fold between the fifteenth day *in utero* and the nineteenth day after birth. Furthermore, this increase occurs in two jumps—one just before birth and the other just before the normal time of weaning (Moog, 1951). The second saltation, which takes place in the nestling, has been examined very closely. It can be made to occur precociously by administration of cortisone or ACTH, and it can be prevented by adrenalectomy at 12 days, i.e., 2–3 days before the rise normally starts (Moog, 1953). In the chick embryo there is just a single period of increase, culminating about a day after hatching (Moog, 1950). This rise can be brought about precociously by administration of hydrocortisone, but this increase in phosphatase is not produced directly by the corticoid. The hormone actually speeds up the total pattern of differentiation of the intestinal epithelium. Phosphatase activity simply goes along as an integrated part of the total pattern of differentiation (Moog and Richardson, 1955).

Thus increase in duodenal phosphatase can serve as an indicator of adrenal activity. The effect of ACTH on duodenal phosphatase has been investigated. The results are summarized in Figure 6. At 15 days there is already an indication of increased secretion by the adrenal cortex. Fifteen days is apparently the earliest stage that results with this test can be expected, because no increase in phosphatase content can be induced earlier than this, even with hydrocortisone. This means that the duodenum is incapable of response earlier than this. Thus it appears that under the influence of exogenous ACTH the adrenal is stimulated to secrete enough corticoid by 15 days of incubation to bring about precocious enzyme production by the duodenum.

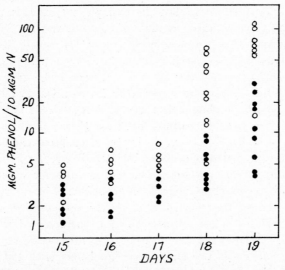

Fig. 6.—The influence of ACTH on phosphatase activity in the duodenum of the chick embryo. *Open circles*, embryos injected with 0.25 mg. ACTH per day beginning at 10 days; *solid circles*, control embryos injected with acidified saline. The ordinate represents phosphatase activity as micrograms of phenol liberated from phenylphosphate per 10 μg. of duodenal nitrogen per half hour. (Moog, unpublished.)

SEGAL suggested that the onset of adrenal function in the rat and chick occurs much later than in the amphibian (Table 1). The indicator of onset of function in young amphibian larvae is the reduction of osmic acid by lipid granules in the cortical cells. The relationship between ACTH and adrenal function is shown very clearly by a simple experiment involving administration of estrogens to the ambient water of stage 25 frog larvae. Starting at this early stage, estrogen treatments induce adrenal hyperplasia and hyperfunction (Segal, 1953). That this estrogen effect is mediated through the release of ACTH by the pituitary is proved by repeating the same experiment on hypophysectomized larvae. In this case no adrenal enlargement occurs (Chang and Witschi,

1955a). Consequently, these experiments show that the estrogen effect, which requires an adrenal responsiveness to ACTH, can be demonstrated as early as standard stage 25. Morphologically this is a stage when the adrenal is still in an unpaired condition without any intermingling of medullary and cortical components. WEISS questioned why, by comparative standards, an amphibian larva just starting to feed would be any less mature than a 13- to 15-day chick embryo. SEGAL answered that this is indicated by the comparative morphogenesis of the glands themselves. They are much less developed in the amphibian larva. SCHNEIDERMAN then questioned the statement of Segal that onset of adrenal function begins at 13–15 days of incubation in the chick. He pointed out that Moog had not said this. Instead, she had said that the very nature of her test made it impossible to demonstrate adrenal func-

TABLE 1

ONSET OF ADRENAL FUNCTION

Animal	Age	Standard Stage*	Reported by
Rat..............	5 days postnatal	35	Gaillard
Chick.............	13–15 days of incubation	34–35	Moog
Amphibian........	*Ca.* 12 days post-fertilization	25	Segal

* Witschi (1956).

tion prior to 15 days. Adrenal function could begin on the eighth or ninth days, but, as far as her test is concerned, onset of function at such an early stage could not be detected.

The question was raised by WILLIER whether the adrenals of the treated animals, and primarily the adrenal cortex, are responsive to administration of ACTH before the anterior pituitary itself is releasing ACTH into the circulation. MOOG replied that this is quite possible. TONUTTI inquired whether she had seen any increase in the size of adrenal cells in her experiments. MOOG replied that the glands had not been examined from that point of view as yet. TONUTTI emphasized that it is important to do so because there is a strong relationship between adrenal stimulation with ACTH and the nuclear size of adrenal cells. The size of the nucleus is a very specific indicator of the action of ACTH on adrenal cells, much more specific, actually, than the weight of the glands. MOOG stated that she intends to examine the adrenals of treated embryos much more closely, to see whether there is any effect of ACTH on them that can be demonstrated directly. Now that a stage has been found where there is no stimulation of growth, she plans to go back from there to determine whether, by other criteria, she can find signs of an earlier stimulation.

Moog also mentioned briefly that, as far as the rat is concerned, an interrelationship between adrenals and the pituitary has been rather clearly shown at about 18 days, i.e., prior to birth, by Kitchell and Wells (1952*a*, *b*).

Hormone production by the medulla of the adrenal glands was then discussed by WILLIER. He pointed out that noradrenalin is produced by the medulla of most fetal mammals, as shown by Shepherd and West (1951). After birth, noradrenalin is present in much lower quantities than at earlier stages of development, whereas adrenalin is now present in considerable amounts. Adrenalin can be detected in the adrenals of chick embryos by the sixth or seventh day of incubation. He raised several questions about the significance of its production so early in development. Is it playing any role in development at this time? Does it have an effect on vasoconstriction at an early stage? Does it play any role in the pattern of sugar metabolism in young embryos? Or is there no release of adrenalin from the medulla at these early stages?

· IV ·

Ontogeny of Selected Endocrine Glands: The Gonads

Attention was next turned to the ontogeny of the gonads by DR. WILLIER. He recalled that this topic has received a great deal of attention because of the pioneer work of Lillie (1916, 1917) on the role of sex hormones in differentiation of sex organs and ducts as demonstrated by his work on the freemartin. BURNS then discussed evidence for the onset of secretory activity in the embryonic testis. He cited three lines of evidence. The first may be called "presumptive evidence" and is clearly of historical interest. It goes back to the time of Bouin and Ancel (1903), who were apparently the first to suggest the hypothesis that, since the embryonic testis possesses interstitial cells like those of the adult testis, it may well be the source of a hormone controlling sex differentiation. This suggestion was based largely on studies of the testes of pig embryos and was proposed thirteen years before Lillie (1916) and Keller and Tandler (1916) presented real evidence for such a theory in their classic studies on the freemartin.

It is now known that, in a number of mammals, cells with the characteristic appearance of interstitial cells are found in the embryonic testis from virtually the beginning of histologic sex differentiation. For example, they have been found by Jost (1946) in the rabbit and by Bouin and Ancel (1903) in the pig. They are present in the testes of young opossums 10 days after birth, at which time the testes are quite embryonic (Burns, 1950, Fig. 1). The testis cords at this time are still solid and almost unconvoluted, retaining the primitive arrangement of simple arches or loops. This arrangement leaves a large interior space occupied by large numbers of interstitial cells which are intermingled with the stromal tissue. This condition obtains at a stage of development when the external genitalia are morphologically indifferent, as is the urinogenital sinus. The first prostatic buds do not make their appearance until about 7 days after this stage, and the paired sex ducts are present in a sexually undifferentiated condition only. In fact, the

Müllerian ducts have but recently established contact with the wall of the urinogenital sinus. Administration of estradiol propionate from birth onward largely or entirely abolishes this interstitium (Burns, 1956*b*).

The second line of évidence for the interstitial function of the embryonic testis is found in the results of early castration. Successful castration has now been achieved in embryos of three species of mammal—the rabbit (Jost, 1947*b*), the mouse (Raynaud and Frilley, 1947), and the rat (Wells, 1950). In general, castration prior to morphologic sex differentiation is followed in the male by an almost complete failure of sex differentiation. The male duct system (Wolffian duct derivatives) atrophies and disappears; prostatic glands fail to develop, and the urinogenital sinus is of female type. The external genitalia also assume the female form. Moreover, in the absence of the embryonic testis the Müllerian duct derivatives persist and are well developed. Castrate males thus eventually come to resemble closely normal females. Evidently, the embryonic testis is the controlling influence in somatic sex differentiation in mammals, and presumably it is the interstitial cells of the testis that are involved. In rabbit embryos, castration as early as the twentieth day of gestation has all the effects mentioned above. However, the effects of castration are progressive, depending on the time the operation is carried out. The effects are limited to a fairly narrow period when morphologic sex differentiation is most active. For example, if rabbit embryos are not castrated until the twenty-third day of gestation, the results are slight; male parts are all present, although they may be somewhat undersized. Castration on the twenty-second day leads to serious deficiencies in the male genital tract, while castration on day 21, or especially on day 20, is followed by almost total suppression of male development. (For summary and references consult Willier, 1955.)

A few words are in order concerning the point that it is probably the interstitial cells of the embryonic testis which are responsible for its effects on genital development. This is best illustrated by certain other experiments of Jost. After hypophysectomy of the rabbit embryo by decapitation, there is a distinct arrest of development of the male genital tract, although the consequences are by no means as severe as after early castration. Examination of the testes of hypophysectomized males reveals that there is an important reduction in the number and size of the interstitial cells present. The defective development of the genital tract in hypophysectomized males is correlated with failure of the interstitium to develop normally (Jost, 1951, 1953).

Another interesting experiment yields evidence on this point of a different sort. When the embryonic testicle of a young rat at the beginning of its sexual differentiation is transplanted between the lobules of the seminal vesicle of an adult castrate male after castration atrophy of the seminal vesicle has occurred, a remarkable thing is seen. In a short time there is complete recovery of the epithelium of the seminal vesicle in the immediate vicinity of the grafted testis, which appears to be producing a substance not distinguishable from the adult male hormone as far as its effects on the vesicle epithelium are concerned. Furthermore, histologic examination of the grafted testis reveals that interstitial cells not only are present but are actually considerably hypertrophied under the influence of the host hypophysis (Jost, 1948; Jost and Colonge, 1949).

These are not the only experiments that could be cited, but they are sufficient evidence for two conclusions: (1) the embryonic testis is producing an androgenic hormone from a very early stage of its development, and (2) it is, in all probability, the interstitial cells that produce this substance. The results of the castration experiments where organs developing at a distance from the site of the testis are strongly affected by castration would indicate that the hormone is normally being released into the blood stream. The external genitalia and other structures far removed from the gonad are among those strongly affected by castration.

The effects of embryonic castration, on the whole, are of the same nature in the chick with one very important exception, namely, that it is the *ovary* which is the more active gonad during the period of sexual differentiation in birds (Wolff and Wolff, 1951). The effects of castration of male embryos are relatively slight in the case of birds, whereas the effects of castration of the female are extremely marked. There is no clue as to why the results should be exactly transposed in birds as compared with mammals, although it should be noted that the sex chromosome mechanism is also reversed in the two classes (males are XY in composition in mammals, but are XX in composition in birds). Perhaps this is in some way the explanation for the fact that in mammals it is the *testis* which exerts the predominant influence in somatic sex differentiation, whereas in birds it seems to be the *ovary*.

WEISS inquired concerning the situation in fish. BURNS commented that the gonads of fish are very elongated and are closely applied to the kidneys; hence embryonic castration of fish would be very difficult to perform for technical reasons. WEISS insisted that there have been cases of testes removal in various fishes. BURNS admitted this but stated that such operations were performed only on adults and hence were not pertinent to the present discussion.

Lillie's classical illustration of the freemartin was then exhibited by WILLIER (Lillie, 1917, Fig. 4). It shows twin cattle *in utero.* They are dizygotic twins, a male and a female, developing simultaneously. Their circulatory systems have been injected to demonstrate that a vascular connection exists between the extra-embryonic membranes of the two twins. Thus there is ample opportunity for exchange of blood between the male and female fetuses and hence for the exchange of any molecules present in the two circulations, including hormones. Actually, so far as sex hormones are concerned, there appears to be a one-way effect of the male twin on the female twin. Interstitial cells appear in the testes of the male before they appear in the ovary of the female. Thus there is a precocious formation of the cells in the testis which are concerned with the production of male hormone. Consequently, the male hormone is carried into the female partner rather early, and it acts to inhibit female differentiation of the gonad by preventing formation of the ovarian cortex. As a rule, a testis develops in the genetic female. The latter is referred to as the "freemartin."

BURNS pointed out the parallel between the results in the freemartin, where the testes of one twin dominate development of the ovaries of the other via their hormones, and the role of the testis in sex differentiation as demonstrated by castration experiments performed on fetal mammals. It is evident that the male gonad of mammals is active in an endocrine way during fetal stages, whereas the ovary is not.

WILLIER commented on the fact that there is no effect in cattle if two female fetuses develop in the uterus simultaneously, or if two male fetuses develop simultaneously, at least as far as sex differentiation is concerned. More recently, Billingham *et al.* (1952, 1956) have shown that it is possible to graft skin from one twin onto the other in postnatal stages when they are associated with each other *in utero* in such a way that they possess a common circulation. This is not possible with ordinary siblings. Sharing a common circulation during fetal development enables the twins to tolerate grafts which ordinarily they would not accept. Blood cells are also exchanged under these conditions. Irwin (1949) and his group have shown that erythrocyte antigens may be identical in the twins which shared a common circulation. Thus studies involving freemartins become more and more complex as knowledge increases. The pioneer work of Lillie constantly paves the way for investigations of the nature of those mentioned above, and it is the starting point for those seeking interpretations of the results obtained in a variety of directions.

WILLIER showed an illustration of a testis formed by transformation of the freemartin gonad (Willier, 1921). The seminiferous tubules are typical in structure, except that they do not contain germ cells. Typical Sertoli cells are present. Here and there are cells which he interprets as interstitial cells. He contrasted its appearance with that of a normal testis of corresponding age which contains typical seminiferous cords and occasional primordial germ cells.

PRICE then discussed her studies on sex differentiation in the rat by the application of organ culture methods. An important aspect of this problem—the question of whether fetal rat testes secrete hormone—was resolved by Wells and his collaborators (Wells, 1950, 1957; Wells and Fralick, 1951), who succeeded in castrating extra-uterinized fetuses. They found that rat testes secrete a hormone which they concluded stimulates growth of the accessory reproductive glands of the male. However, they could not castrate fetuses that were younger than 18 days, which represents a relatively advanced stage in sex differentiation. Price selected the watch-glass method of organ culture for her studies on sex differentiation because it has several distinct advantages: (1) entire fetal reproductive tracts can be isolated at early stages of development and cultured on clots in which the medium can be controlled; (2) surgical procedures, such as gonad removal, can be done with a minimum of trauma; (3) complicating factors, such as the presence of other fetal endocrine glands and maternal and placental hormones, are avoided; (4) the explants can be seen so clearly on the semisolid clots that development or retrogression of the ducts and the development of the primordia of the seminal vesicles can be observed and photographed from day to day.

She explanted approximately 300 male and female fetal tracts, ranging from $13\frac{1}{2}$ to $18\frac{1}{2}$ days in age, and cultured them from 1 to 6 days with transfers. The tracts, which represented all stages from before sex differentiation had occurred to advanced stages of differentiation, were cultured under several experimental conditions: with both gonads present; with only one gonad present; with no gonads present; with gonads of the opposite sex; with no gonads present, but with exogenous hormone in the medium; etc. Her chief purpose was to determine whether fetal gonads are producing hormones which affect the morphogenesis of the tracts and, if so, to compare those effects with the results obtained by the addition of exogenous hormones. The standard medium is cock plasma (the results are no different with capon plasma) and chick embryo extract, to which, in some experiments, micropellets of testosterone or estradiol are added. Her results leave some important questions unanswered, but at least a part of the problem has been clarified (Price and Pannabecker, 1956; Pannabecker, 1957; Price, 1957).

Her results can be summarized by reference to her schematic figure (Fig. 7). If a male reproductive tract $17\frac{1}{2}$ days old (A) is explanted on standard medium and cultured for 4 days, it remains essentially the same size or becomes smaller, but development continues. Seminal vesi-

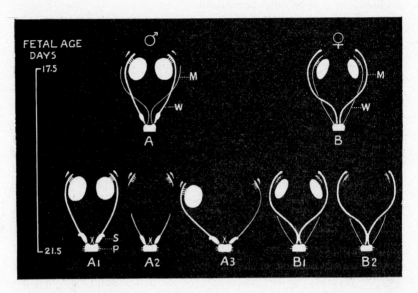

Fig. 7.—Diagrammatic representation of reproductive tracts of male and female rat fetuses. A and $B:$ male and female tracts at $17\frac{1}{2}$ days, the age of explantation. *A1, A2, A3, B1, B2:* tracts cultured for 4 days. *M:* Müllerian ducts; *W:* Wolffian ducts; *S:* seminal vesicles; *P:* prostate. Redrawn from Price and Pannabecker (1956).

cles form from dilatations on the Wolffian ducts, and prostatic buds grow out from the urinogenital sinus; Müllerian ducts retrogress anteriorly, but the utriculus prostaticus forms posteriorly ($A1$). The results are the same when both testes are removed by carefully severing the efferent ducts and then replacing them. This demonstrates that the trauma caused by the removal of the testes does not produce general Wolffian duct retrogression. The same results are obtained if only one testis is replaced. Thus one testis can insure normal development. Complete absence of the testes ($A2$) results in Wolffian duct retrogression and failure of development of the seminal vesicles and some of the prostatic buds. These experiments indicate that fetal rat testes secrete a substance which diffuses from them in organ culture and causes the maintenance of the Wolffian ducts and the development of the primordia of the seminal vesicles and some of the prostatic buds. A further experiment (*A3*) provides interesting evidence concerning the limits of diffusion. When the two sides of the tract are widely separated, development on the side with the testis continues normally, whereas on the contralateral side the Wolffian duct tends to retrogress and the seminal vesicle is smaller or totally lacking. It seems probable that the hormone from the testis is diffusing into the medium and is also passing down the duct system. A unilateral effect was also reported by Wells and Fralick (1951) for some unilaterally castrated fetal rats and by Jost (1950) for unilaterally castrated fetal rabbits. Jost interpreted his findings as evidence that in vivo the hormone from fetal testes migrates along the genital tract and reaches some parts of the reproductive system in that way as well as by circulatory pathways. A fourth type of experiment, not illustrated in Figure 7, shows that when testes are absent, but testosterone micropellets are present in the medium, the Wolffian ducts, seminal vesicles, and prostates develop normally, as in *A1*. This is not interpreted as evidence that fetal testes necessarily secrete testosterone. The nature of the fetal hormone is not known. In these experiments the dependence of the male Wolffian ducts and primordia of the seminal vesicles and prostate on testis-secreted hormone or on exogenous androgen seems clear.

By contrast, the hormone independence of the Müllerian ducts of the female, once they are well established, is clearly shown in Figure 7. When the tract of a $17\frac{1}{2}$-day female (*B*) is cultured for 4 days, development of the posterior ends of the ducts continues, and the uterovaginal canal forms (*B1*). Removal of the ovaries (*B2*) has no effect on the Müllerian ducts, which appear similar to those in *B1*. In both cases the Wolffian ducts retrogress, and a few prostatic buds develop (a stock of rats which have spontaneously developing female prostates was used).

This brief and simplified summary suggests that in the fetal rat the testes may normally be secreting hormone which determines the retention of the Wolffian ducts and the development of the primordia of the accessory glands. The ovary, on the contrary, may not be producing a hormone, or, if it is, the hormone is not necessary for the maintenance of the Müllerian ducts. However, the retrogression of the male Müllerian ducts and of the female Wolffian ducts must be considered. These aspects, as well as gonad and prostatic development in culture, are treated in detail by Pannabecker (1957) and can be discussed here only briefly. The Müllerian ducts of males retrogress anteriorly and develop the prostatic utricle posteriorly under all the culture conditions. They are not retained when testes are removed, nor is retrogression hastened by testosterone; in fact, some stimulation is found. The Müllerian ducts of females are not inhibited by testes placed against them or by testosterone; instead, stimulation was apparent in both experimental conditions. Female Wolffian ducts undergo slow retrogression in younger explants but retrogress rapidly in older ones. They are somewhat stimulated by testes and testosterone, but they are not completely retained under these conditions, and no seminal vesicles form. There are possible explanations for some of these findings, but more research will be necessary before the questions can be answered. However, from these experiments it seems probable that sex differentiation of the ducts and accessory glands in the fetal rat is related to the presence of testis-secreted hormone in the male and the absence of such a hormone in the female. Jost (1950, 1957) has reported convincing evidence that this is the case in the rabbit.

BURNS remarked that it was very gratifying to him to see that the rat embryo comes nearer and nearer to being brought into line with the rabbit. In spite of the fact that everyone knows that species differences exist and group differences which may sometimes be very great, it is always disturbing when contradictory results are obtained.

PRICE pointed out that the cause of Müllerian duct retrogression in male rats is still a question. Jost (1950, 1957) seems convinced that the Müllerian ducts are inhibited by fetal testis hormone in the rabbit. He reported a case in which a fetal testis was introduced into the abdominal cavity of a female and caused localized retrogression of the Müllerian duct. In her explants, by contrast, when testes which are secreting hormone are placed against female Müllerian ducts, there is localized stimulation. BURNS also considers the Müllerian ducts to present a special problem because of the fact that in mammalian embryos it is very difficult or impossible to inhibit them with testosterone or any other known pure androgen. By contrast, in birds and in amphibians these structures may be completely obliterated by treatment with male hormone. This is another striking example of the contradictions that may be encountered in different groups. It is a puzzling situation, but it may only mean in some cases that no one appreciates all the conditions necessary for development or inhibition of mammalian Müllerian ducts. Just a few years ago it was believed that embryonic mammalian gonads also constituted a complete exception in being non-reactive to hormones. Now, in the opossum at any rate, it is known that they are reactive under the proper experimental conditions.

PRICE then commented that perhaps it is not too surprising that testosterone stimulates male and female Müllerian ducts in her explants because she has been able to observe the Müllerian ducts actually splitting away from the Wolffian duct at the posterior end, suggesting a common origin. She pointed out that this agrees with the observations of Gruenwald (1941), who made similar observations in the human and in the chick. BURNS stated that this might be expected to occur, especially with a high dose, since different thresholds might be involved, and that testosterone in large doses stimulates the Müllerian ducts of the opossum greatly. This is an example of the so-called paradoxical effect. But it does not do so in very low dosages. He inquired what happens to the Müllerian ducts in Price's cultures with a very low dose of testosterone. He pointed out that in many experiments on the opossum (more recent results of which will be described later on) extremely small doses are far more effective than huge doses, which cause all kinds of abnormalities which confuse the picture and even introduce results which are diametrically opposite to the expected results. PRICE stated that it was with the hope of obtaining a physiologic level that she explanted fetal testes against female tracts. But, of course, there is no reason for thinking that the threshold of stimulation and the threshold of inhibition are the same in male Wolffian ducts and in female Wolffian ducts, in male Müllerian ducts and in female Müllerian ducts.

WILLIER then asked whether homologous ducts in genetic males and genetic females actually do give a different response to the same experimental conditions. PRICE answered that there are definite differences between male and female Wolffian ducts and male and female Müllerian ducts and that some of these can be attributed to a difference in the male and female genetic constitution. BURNS added that this is just the type of result he obtained some years ago in the opossum (Burns, 1942) and which has been described in more detail recently (Burns, 1956a). It holds true for a variety of sex primordia. In young opossums of the same litter, treated with male or with female hormone under identical experimental conditions as to dosage, timing, and duration of treatment, male primordia under the influence of male hormone always attain a much greater size in male subjects than do the corresponding primordia in female subjects. Conversely, prospective female structures under the influence of female hormone become larger in female subjects than in males.

The question was then raised by SEGAL whether available information is definite enough to state that the secretion of the embryonic gonad is identical with the hormone produced by the adult gonad. He seemed convinced that this might be probable and suggested that the one discordant note is an experiment of Jost (1947*a*), in which he found that a deposit of crystalline testosterone does not act like an embryonic testis in maintaining the Wolffian ducts. PRICE stated that she did not know what hormone is secreted by the fetal testes but that testosterone substituted for it, so far as the Wolffian ducts and primordia of accessory glands are concerned. She stated that Jost reported that crystalline testosterone maintains the Wolffian ducts but does not cause retrogression of the Müllerian ducts. BURNS added that, as far as the prostate and other structures in opossums are concerned, crystalline hormones substitute completely for the absence of the testes but do not cause the inhibition of ducts, which seems to be in a separate category. Burns does not believe that anyone would hold out for identity in any literal sense of the word. Yet that is the only variable in the physiologic effect.

An interesting question was then raised by WEISS. He inquired whether testosterone is now considered to be exactly identical with the secretion of the adult testis. SEGAL stated that it has been isolated from testis extracts and has also been recovered from blood taken from the testicular vein. But BURNS answered that it is not so considered, to his knowledge. He pointed out that there are many effects of the adult hormone even beyond the confines of the genital system. There is certainly marked physiologic similarity, but hardly identity. WEISS then stated that if this is so, the inability to reproduce an embryonic effect by a crystal of testosterone does not necessarily indicate that the embryonic and adult hormones are different. The use of testosterone crystals simply cannot prove or disprove the identity or non-identity of embryonic and adult hormones.

WILLIER suggested that the preponderance of the evidence indicates that they are similar, if not identical, whatever their nature may be. He mentioned that Witschi (1950) had argued that the effect of a bit of fetal testis on the epithelium of a seminal vesicle to which it had been added (Jost, 1948) is an inductor effect rather than a hormonal effect. But, since the same kind of effect can be produced by administration of sex hormones to the castrated adult rat, the response of the seminal vesicle to the transplanted fetal testis is the same as to a synthetic hormone.

SEGAL concluded that the over-all evaluation of Jost's work leads to the belief that a crystalline hormone does not act like the embryonic testis. BURNS stated that he would prefer to qualify this remark by adding that the crystalline hormone (testosterone) acts very much like the embryonic testis except in the case of the Müllerian ducts, as mentioned above.

SEGAL then recalled that Jost's work on rabbits suggested that mammalian embryos deprived of their gonads, either testes or ovaries, would develop the somatic habitus of the female. This implies that the syndrome in humans known as "ovarian agenesis" should include both genetic males and females. When Barr and his associates (Moore, Graham, and Barr, 1953) described a sexual dimorphism in the nuclei of epithelial cells of human skin, it became possible to ascertain the genetic sex of humans exhibiting this syndrome. When a large group of patients —all raised and living as women—was tested by this means, it was found that a large percentage of them were, in fact, genetic males. Although these individuals possessed no gonads, there was no doubt but that they were sex-reversed with respect to their secondary sex characters.

Attention was then called by WILLIER to the work of Wolff and Haffen (1952) in relation to the question as to whether or not sex hormones of the embryo and those of the adult are similar or identical. They cultivated an embryonic testis in vitro with a bit of embryonic ovarian tissue and found that an ovarian cortex forms on the testis under these conditions. Direct contact between the two explanted gonads is not necessary to achieve this result. Since the same result can be produced by injections of female sex hormone into male embryos, the similarity, if not identity, of action in the two cases is evident. The question of the quantity of hormone produced at these early stages was also raised by WILLIER. The amount of hormone produced at first seems to be very low. This is indicated by some of his own experiments. When little bits of adult testis or adult ovary are transplanted to the chorio-allantoic membrane of host embryos, the development of the sex of the host is not modified (Willier, 1927). Or if a sexually indifferent gonad rudiment is transplanted to the chorio-allantoic membrane of a host embryo, the sex hormones of the host have no effect on the graft. But more recently it has been demonstrated that if a larger quantity of gonadal tissue is grafted to the chorio-allantoic membrane, hormones produced by the graft can cause sex reversal in the host. Such an approach presumably increases the quantity of hormone produced by the graft above the threshold involved in sex reversal.

PRICE again recalled that Jost (1953) had reported unilateral effects in unilaterally castrated fetal rabbits and that he had suggested that the hormone level was higher on the testis side because of migration of the hormone along the genital tract. She again recalled that diffusion of hormone from the fetal testis was clearly evident in her explants. WIL-LIER agreed that there is more and more evidence accumulating all the time that, when an endocrine gland is placed close to its receptor, the former affects the latter by diffusion of its hormone through the inter-vening tissues. At a stage in development when the receptor will not re-spond if located at a distance from the endocrine gland, it will respond if placed close to the latter. This can only mean that low concentrations of hormone are released at first. The concentration is too low to have an effect via the circulatory system but is high enough to have an effect by diffusion to nearby regions. WEISS pointed out that this is simply an-other way of saying that the receptor organ responds above a certain threshold regardless of the route by which the threshold is reached, whether through the circulation or through the tissues spaces. He also stated that the experiments in which unilateral effects were obtained in unilaterally castrated fetal rabbits also support this conclusion. WILLIER then commented on the fact that this concept of diffusion of hormones from their point of origin has appeared in the literature only quite re-cently. It was first established by Etkin (1939), who transplanted a thyroid gland near the anterior pituitary, and vice versa, and obtained precocious stimulation of the thyroid. Development of this concept has been reviewed (Willier, 1955). It has certain connotations for general thinking about various problems concerned with the release and action of hormones. More recently, Dossel (1958) has examined this situation in chick embryos. He isolates the thyroid vesicle in early stages (from 4- to $4\frac{1}{2}$-day donors) and transplants it, together with some mesen-chyme, to the head or to the coelom of an intact host embryo. The thy-roid tissue that develops from the implanted vesicle 7 or 8 days later forms a single spherical mass rather than two approximately equal masses, as in the normal embryo. It was thought that the host would then have a complement of thyroid tissue equivalent in mass to that possessed by two normal embryos of similar age. Instead, the combina-tion of the mass of thyroid tissue of the implant and of the normally situated thyroids of the host is only slightly, but not significantly, more than the total mass of tissue of the normal embryo of similar age. This regulation always involves a decrease in the mass of the host's own thy-roid, whether the original implant is placed in the head or in the coelom. In 11-day hosts the aggregate is only about 107.9 per cent of normal; in 12-days hosts, 103.6 per cent; and in 13-day hosts, about 104 per cent.

It is believed that this regulation is due in part to a restricted output of thyrotrophic hormone, for which host and implant thyroids compete.

WEISS then inquired when pituitary control over gonad activity began. BURNS replied that Jost (1953) has evidence in rabbit embryos that the pituitary is quite active during the period when the secretory activity of the testis and the process of sex differentiation are most marked. KOLLROS called attention to the work of Fugo (1940), which shows a reduction of intertubular tissue in the testis of pituitaryless chick embryos as early as the thirteenth day of incubation. WILLIER stated that he had been toying with the idea that the anterior pituitary may be releasing its gonadotrophic hormones earlier than hitherto suspected in very small quantities, which somehow or other are utilized by the developing gonads. Willier also stated that Fugo's results should be more thoroughly investigated and controlled by administering gonadotrophins to pituitaryless embryos to determine whether the condition of the gonads could be restored to normal. Preliminary attempts in this direction have been made by Vogel (1957). KOLLROS stated that if the absence of the pituitary causes a change in the normal pattern of gonad differentiation, it is implied that the gonad is already sensitive to pituitary hormones by that time. He inquired whether there is any evidence that it is sensitive earlier. According to WILLIER, no information is available on this point.

WEISS commented that his interest in the time of onset of pituitary control over gonad activity was simply to determine whether there is a sufficient safety margin there, i.e., whether the pituitary is already active by the time the gonad takes up its function as the next station down the line. Returning to the question of the quantity of hormone produced early in the development of endocrine organs, he pointed out that the statement that less hormone is produced earlier and more later does not necessarily mean that the individual cell is less effective from the start. It may only mean that there are fewer cells producing the hormone initially. The individual cell that is releasing gonadotrophins may be fully efficient right from the start; more hormone would be released as more cells become capable of secretion. But perhaps the individual cell does increase its output with time. WILLIER suggested that, although the total number of cells does increase with time to some extent, the increase is probably not sufficient to account for increased hormone production with time. According to KOLLROS, the work of Etkin (1955) and others shows clearly that the thyroid gland grows remarkably in the stages preceding metamorphic climax in amphibians and that, during the climax phases, cytologic evidence points to an increased secretory activity of the gland.

SEGAL then mentioned that there is an indication that the fetal gonad is at least responsive to gonadotrophic stimulation in the human. The interstitium is obviously stimulated at the time of birth, most likely as a result of its exposure to chorionic gonadotrophins *in utero*. Shortly thereafter, there is a regression of the interstitium, again indicating that the initial stimulation was the result of gonadotrophic stimulation. He pointed out, in relation to this comment, that it is curious that no observation has been reported about the condition of the testes in newborn anencephalic monsters.

TONUTTI discussed this matter in more detail. He stated that the peak of development of the interstitial cells in the human testis occurs at a length of 10 cm. Regression begins before birth. He questioned whether it is actually the chorionic gonadotrophin which stimulates these cells. SEGAL commented that this parallels the level of gonadotrophins, and TONUTTI agreed that this is so at the 10-cm. stage. But he pointed out that regression of the Leydig cells in the fetal testis is not uniform. Even at birth, there is a considerable amount of well-developed Leydig cells present. In cases of hypogonadotrophic hypogonadism, the entire population of Leydig cells shows about the same stage of regression. He called attention to the curious fact that, in spite of the presence of well-developed Leydig cells, the latter are not influencing tubule formation in any obvious way. Ordinarily, when Leydig cells are stimulated by gonadotrophins after birth, they induce tubule formation. Thus the question arises whether the fetal Leydig cells are producing the same hormones as mature Leydig cells of the adult. Recently he observed a five-and-a-half-year-old boy with Leydig cell tumor and pseudo-precocious puberty. Near the tumor the tubules had a diameter of about 130 μ and showed advanced, but not complete, spermatogenesis. At a distance from the tumor the diameter of the tubules was only 70 μ, and the epithelium was immature. The diameter of the tubules in the other testis without tumor was about 60 μ. The tumor appears to produce testosterone; this may be concluded from a high peak of androsterone in the chromatogram of the 17-ketosteroids. BURNS suggested that perhaps there is a question concerning the time at which the tubules become sensitive. TONUTTI answered that they are always sensitive after birth. WILLIER inquired about the appearance of secondary sex characters in this boy. TONUTTI answered that they are very well developed. This boy has a bone age of about twelve years. 17-Ketosteroids before operation amounted to 8–10 mg/24 hours. After semicastration they fell to 3 mg/24 hours. These are the data of Schmidt and Tonutti (1956). GAILLARD then asked what happened to the development of the boy after removal of the tumor. TONUTTI replied that the patient lost his pubic hair but continued to gain in height. The testis seemed to become somewhat larger. A fairly great number of normal Leydig cells are present in both testes. It appears that this boy is changing from a precocious pseudo-puberty into a true, but still incomplete, precocious puberty. The observations of Wilkins and Cara (1954) are also pertinent; they involve cases of the adrenogenital syndrome. It appears that androgens produced by a pathologic tissue mature the organism as reflected by bone age and that, if a certain degree of somatic maturation is reached, the hypophysis begins production of gonadotrophins.

PRICE asked how long before birth the prostate gland of the human male becomes hypertrophied. She thought information about this might suggest great activity of the fetal testis. TONUTTI had no information about this. MOOG inquired whether such a change in the prostate gland might possibly be due to androgens from the fetal adrenal cortex rather than from the testis. She stated that the fetal cortex does very definitely produce androgen, according to the work of Bernirschke and Bloch and their co-workers (Bernirschke *et al.*, 1956; Bloch *et al.*, 1956). Since there is so much of this tissue, there might well be a strong androgenic stimulation from this source. Consequently, she suggested that it would be difficult to draw any conclusions about the activity of the fetal testis from observations on the development of the prostate. PRICE then stated that she was simply interested in learning whether there is any relation between the Leydig cells of the fetal testis and hypertrophy of the prostate. TONUTTI informed her that the peak of development of the Leydig cells is much earlier than the development of the prostate. It corresponds with the differentiation of the cells in the hypophysis, i.e., it occurs at about the 10-cm. stage. WILLIER then suggested that Moog's method of studying the time at which the adrenal cortex can respond to stimulation by ACTH is the approach indicated here for study of the problem of time of onset of gonadotrophic stimulation. MOOG inquired whether chorionic gonadotrophin would not complicate the picture, to which WILLIER replied in the affirmative, provided that they get through the placenta.

· V ·

Ontogeny of Selected Endocrine Glands: The Parathyroids

The development and secretory activity of the parathyroids was next discussed by DR. GAILLARD. He attempted to get some information about the secretory activity of the parathyroid glands during development of the chick embryo with the aid of organ culture methods. First, he had to develop a method for dissection of the parathyroid glands. They cannot be isolated by a frontal approach but can be obtained by a dorsal approach. It is then rather easy to excise the glands even from an 8-day embryo. In order to check the secretory activity of the parathyroid tissue, the gland is placed *in toto* on top of a square fragment of parietal bone excised from the center of the actively growing bone of a mouse embryo near term. As a rule, the combined culture of active parathyroid and bone tissue leads, within 3–6 days after explantation, to a definite lacunar bone resorption. This never occurs in control explants of bone tissue without parathyroid tissue. As another type of control experiment, parietal bone is combined with explants of thyroid gland tissue. In this case bone resorption does not occur; on the contrary, there is an enormous amount of ectopic bone formed inside the inner periosteum (Gaillard, 1955a, b). Summarizing the results of a great number of experiments, it can be said that the parathyroid gland tissue of chick embryos is active in this way from the eighth day of incubation on. When the influence of the gland on the bone tissue is examined in more detail, it is found that the first change is a relatively intense staining reaction of the bone matrix with the periodic Schiff reaction after only 2 days of culturing. At the same time the number of cells in the inner periosteum increases considerably, and they begin to encapsulate the parathyroid explant, which is placed in close contact with the inner periosteum. Moreover, cinemicrographic records of a number of explants reveal an increased mobility of the intertrabecular cells. As a rule, some resorption of bone matrix is found even when typical osteoclasts are not visible. After 5–7 days of cultivation, a very intensive bone resorption occurs, and many giant multinuclear osteoclasts are then present. In histologic sections the osteoclasts are found in close contact with spicules of bone, and brush borders are evident. From these experiments it appears quite certain that, from the eighth day on, the parathyroid tissue is capable of releasing some agent which causes the bone matrix to change its chemical composition; this is then followed by intensive osteoclastic resorption. The same kind of effect is found after combined cultivation of parathyroid tissue taken from human newborns, as well as after the addition of commercial parathormone from Eli Lilly and Company (Gaillard, 1955*a*, *b*, 1957). GAILLARD stated that it was Barnicot (1948) who first described the same type of results in vivo and that Chang (1951), working in Bloom's laboratory, later extended Barnicot's work. However, he emphasized that the possibility exists in their work that antigen-antibody reactions might complicate the interpretation of the results, whereas, in the absence of these reactions in vitro, misinterpretations are much less likely.

WILLIER recalled that he had presented some arguments (Willier, 1955) in favor of early secretion of parathormone by the mammalian fetus. Chief among these is the fact that the parathyroid glands assume adult histologic characteristics rather early in development, actually very shortly after they are detached from the pharyngeal pouches. GAILLARD mentioned that it is difficult to get evidence of secretory activity from the histologic picture encountered in avian parathyroid tissue. Morphologic evidence of a secretory cycle is much less pronounced in this gland than in the anterior pituitary, for example.

WEISS then inquired whether the parathyroids of embryonic stages act through the same mechanism as in later stages. GAILLARD replied that he could say only that approximately the same kind of effects occur in hyperparathyroidism, although they are not encountered simultaneously in the entire skeleton. At least in the beginning of the disease, there are certain sites of preference where bone resorption obviously occurs more readily. WEISS then inquired whether the hormone acts through its effects on some of the cells of the bone or whether it acts directly on the ground substance. GAILLARD answered that it is his impression that its action is directly on the bone matrix; however, he could not be certain that the cells around the matrix were not involved in some way. It appears quite certain that the immediate effect is not on osteoclastic activity. The initial changes in the bone occur without any obvious activity of osteoclasts. WEISS then asked whether its effect might be on the collagen. GAILLARD answered that if collagen is interpreted as part of the whole system of structural relations between collagenous fibers and the adjacent mucoproteins, it is probably the mucoprotein part of the system which is attacked primarily. TONUTTI then mentioned that Engfeldt and Zetterström (1954) believe that parathormone acts primarily on bone cells. They reported that microchemical reactions in the bone are first detectable 18 hours after a single injection of parathormone into the intact animal, whereas cellular reactions are recognizable only 6 hours after injection. GAILLARD stated emphatically that this is certainly not the case in explants. Here the first reaction occurs in the bone, and the osteoclasts react only secondarily. Osteoblasts are not influenced at all because, in the same explant, osteoblastic formation of bone occurs a short distance from the explant of parathyroid tissue at the same time that resorption occurs near the latter. Only fibrocyte-like cells are present in the vicinity of the parathyroid explant; no osteoblasts are present there. Active osteoclasts are seen from the fifth or sixth day on.

WEISS then inquired whether osteoclasts and osteoblasts are the same cells in different stages of operation, as McLean and Bloom assumed (McLean, 1943). GAILLARD stated that they assume a fusion of osteoblasts, leading to formation of osteoclasts. He also stated that his moving picture provides no information about the origin of osteoclasts. Within a few hours they are present as very actively moving cells. They move from one place to another, settle down on a piece of bone matrix, do their job, and move again to another fragment of bone matrix. The culture media always become exceedingly acid during cultivation of parathyroids. When parathormone was used on cultures, the most active concentrations were found to be between 1.5 and 0.02 IU/cc. There is some evidence that this hormone is a protein, but there is no information as yet about its structure. Eli Lilly and Company is trying to prepare a crystalline parathormone.

· VI ·

Endocrine Organs of Arthropods, with Special Emphasis on Insects

The nature of the endocrine organs of insects and other arthropods was reviewed by SCHNEIDERMAN, to provide background information for any comments to be made by him in the future. There are three principal endocrine organs in insects that are known at present: the brain, the prothoracic glands, and the corpus allatum. The brain contains several groups of neurosecretory cells which produce an endocrine substance which may be called the "brain hormone." In some insects these neurosecretory cells send their axons to an organ just behind the brain, the corpus cardiacum, where they release neurosecretory material. The corpus cardiacum (or corpora cardiaca, for they are commonly paired organs) serves as a storage place for neurosecretory substance in the same way as the sinus gland of crustaceans or the posterior pituitary of vertebrates. Presumably, it releases its storage products into the blood, possibly in modified form. The corpus cardiacum is of nervous origin, as is the neurohypophysis of vertebrates.

The corpus allatum is found in close association with the corpus cardiacum and, like the latter, is commonly paired. It is of ectodermal origin and produces a hormone which may be called the "corpus allatum hormone" or, better, the "juvenile hormone," for reasons which will be clear shortly.

The prothoracic gland, a diffuse glandular organ made up of conspicuous large cells and commonly located in the prothorax, is an important and very ancient endocrine structure. It produces a hormone which will be called the "prothoracic gland hormone," hereafter referred to as "PGH."

The way in which these endocrine glands work can best be understood by considering what happens to an epidermal cell in an insect when it is exposed to these hormones. PGH is the growth and molting hormone of insects. In the presence of this hormone the insect will grow and molt. In its absence, growth and molting cease. This appears to be true in all insects thus far studied. In response to stimulation by

PGH, an epidermal cell secretes a new cuticle and molts. The kind of cuticle that the epidermal cell secretes indicates the stage of differentiation of that cell. The cuticle of the epidermal cell is thus a fingerprint of the cell's morphogenetic potentialities. The kind of cuticle that the epidermal cell produces depends on whether or not corpus allatum hormone is present. In the case of silkworm larvae, for example, if the epidermal cell is exposed to PGH only, the insect as a whole will progress in the adult direction, and the epidermal cells will produce a cuticle with adult characteristics. If, however, there is present, in addition to PGH, a large amount of corpus allatum hormone, this same epidermal cell will produce a larval cuticle. Finally, if PGH is present together with a small amount of juvenile hormone, the very same epidermal cell will make a pupal cuticle. If the differences between the scaly cuticle of a moth, the hard, tanned cuticle of a pupa, and the smooth cuticle of a caterpillar are recalled, it will immediately be recognized that in these different hormonal milieus the epidermal cell is making very different kinds of cuticle. Thus the basic stimulus for growth and differentiation of epidermal cells (and the rest of the insect as well) is PGH, but the direction of development—whether larval, pupal, or adult—is determined by another hormone, the juvenile hormone of the corpus allatum. If there is a great deal of juvenile hormone present, a larval cuticle is produced; if a small amount is present, a pupal cuticle; and if none at all is present, an adult cuticle.

The brain hormone is a trophic hormone and has as its specific target the prothoracic glands. The brain hormone stimulates the latter to secrete PGH, presumably in a way not unlike the stimulation of the adrenal cortex by ACTH.

Postembryonic growth and molting of insects can be understood quite simply in terms of these three hormones. Indeed, there is evidence that even during embryonic life these hormones play a role. For example, some grasshoppers molt about halfway through embryonic life in response to secretion of PGH by the embryonic prothoracic glands.

One of the most striking features of insect development is that growth and molting in insects are cyclical. Periods of active growth and molting alternate with periods of quiescence. The cyclical molting results from the cyclical activity of the neurosecretory cells in the brain. Periodically, these cells are active, and periodically they stimulate the prothoracic glands to secrete PGH. What the cells of the insect do in response to this stimulation depends on the amount of juvenile hormone that is released by the corpora allata. Consider for a moment the commercial silkworm, *Bombyx mori*. During larval life the corpora allata release large amounts of juvenile hormone, and, consequently, every time the larva molts, it molts into a larva. But if the corpora allata are extirpated from the larva at any stage, it promptly molts into the next stage, i.e., into a pupa. This pupal molt presumably reflects the response of the insect to PGH and to small amounts of juvenile hormone remaining even after the allata are removed (Fukuda, 1944). By carefully timed surgical maneuvers it is possible to get a larva to molt in what is apparently the virtual absence of juvenile hormone. Thus C. M. Williams and W. H. Telfer (unpublished) extirpated the corpora allata from a mature *Cecropia* silkworm larva about 2 weeks before pupation was scheduled to occur. Under these conditions, endogenous juvenile hormone soon disappears from the blood of the larva; for, when it molts, it forms a bizarre intermediate between pupa and adult. Apparently, in the absence of the juvenile hormone, some of the epidermal cells go directly from making larval cuticle to making adult cuticle without the intervention of the pupal stage.

It is of some further interest that a larva can be caused to remain a larva long after it should have pupated, by supplying it with juvenile hormone. Whenever most of this hormone is removed, the larva then becomes a pupa. Thus in the normal life of the insect the corpora allata cease secreting at the end of larval life, and the pupal molt ensues. When the next molt occurs, the corpora allata are still inactive, the endogenous juvenile hormone has all disappeared, and the pupa now molts into an adult. Thus the larval, pupal, and adult molts are associated with progressively smaller amounts of juvenile hormone.

A question arises as to whether pupal or adult epidermis can be made to secrete larval cuticle. The answer probably is Yes. Thus Piepho (1939*a, b*) showed that when fragments of pupal integument are implanted into young larvae, in which the juvenile hormone titer is high, a larval cuticle is secreted. Thus the epidermal cells have not reached a morphogenetic dead end when they become adult; they are still capable of producing a juvenile cuticle when exposed to suitable extrinsic stimuli.

So much for the sources and effects of these hormones. Their chemical nature can now be considered. In 1954, after ten years of effort, Peter Karlson and Adolph Butenandt, of the Max-Planck Institute at Tübingen, succeeded in isolating from 500 kg. of commercial silkworms (about 330,000) 25 mg. of a crystalline substance (Butenandt and Karlson, 1954). This substance, when injected in one to ten parts per million, causes insects to molt. Indeed, if it is injected into the isolated pupal abdomen of a *Cecropia* silkworm which contains no endocrine organs, it causes the molt of this structure into an adult abdomen (Williams, 1954). This crystalline material is unquestionably PGH, and Karlson has given it the name "ecdysone" (Karlson, 1956). Fortunately, it is a small molecule and has no nitrogen. Its elementary formula is $C_{18}H_{30}O_4$, and it appears to be an alpha-beta unsaturated ketone with hydroxyl and methyl groups. It is active endocrinologically in virtually all insects that have been studied. Moreover, Karlson has recently isolated ecdysone from crustaceans, in which it apparently controls molting just as it does in insects (Karlson, 1956). Thus it seems fair to say that in an evolutionary sense the prothoracic gland hormone, ecdysone, is probably the oldest hormone that is known, for the insects and the Crustacea must have diverged a long time ago. Indeed, ecdysone probably triggered off molting in the trilobites! Aside from its ancient origin, ecdysone is a significant hormone molecule for another reason; it is responsible for more animal growth in our particular part of the universe than any other molecule.

The juvenile hormone is a molecule of no less interest. It is a conservative factor which permits growth and molting but prevents differentiation. It represents, at least for the insect, the fountain of youth. As long as the insect maintains production of the juvenile hormone, maturity will be delayed. Very recently Carroll Williams (1956) obtained an active extract of juvenile hormone by the simple maneuver of extracting abdomens of male *Cecropia* moths with ether. Why the juvenile hormone should be stored in the abdomen of male moths is not yet known. About 0.2 cc. of clear, yellow oil can be obtained from each abdomen, and this oil has potent juvenile hormone activity. For example, injection of about 0.1 cc. into a silkworm pupa that is about to molt into a moth causes the pupa to molt into another pupa. The extract works not only on silkworms but on all other insects studied. The juvenile hormone, like ecdysone, appears to be a small molecule that is not species-specific.

Nothing is known about the chemical nature of the brain hormone, and all efforts to obtain an active extract of this substance from brains have failed completely. All that is known about the brain hormone is that neurosecretory material from the brain (which may or may not be brain hormone) moves down neurosecretory axons to the corpora cardiaca, where it appears to be stored. Berta Scharrer (1952) has shown that if the connections between the brain and the corpus cardiacum are cut, neurosecretory material accumulates above the point of section.

In the Crustacea, molting is under the control of an organ called the "Y-organ," which is homologous to the prothoracic glands and apparently secretes ecdysone. There are also numerous neurosecretory cells in the brain and associated structures of Crustacea, and these appear to regulate the activity of the Y-organ, perhaps in a fashion similar to the regulation of the activity of the prothoracic gland of insects by the neurosecretory cells of the brain. Growth and molting in the Crustacea are thus under the control of neurosecretory cells and a homologue of the prothoracic glands.

WEISS inquired whether the crustacean glands have actually been tested experimentally for their endocrine functions. This question was raised because Schneiderman had referred to them as "homologues" of insect organs. SCHNEIDERMAN answered that Gabe (1952*a, b, c,* 1953) in Paris, the discoverer of the Y-organ, has shown that this organ resembles the prothoracic glands histologically, and his co-worker Échalier (1954, 1955), has conducted extirpation and implantation experiments which demonstrate that the Y-organ controls molting at least in the decapod Crustacea (see review of Knowles and Carlisle, 1956). Moreover, Karlson (1956) has extracted from the shrimp, *Crangon vulgaris,* a hormone which causes insects to molt, presumably ecdysone from the Y-organ.

SCHNEIDERMAN also mentioned that there are certainly other hormones in insects that have received less study. For example, the ovaries of many insects appear to produce a hormone that acts on the corpora allata; if an insect is castrated, there is a hypertrophy of the corpora allata. He also amplified further the analogy between the corpus cardiacum–corpus allatum complex of insects and the neurohypophysis-adenohypophysis complex of the vertebrates (Wigglesworth, 1934; Hanström, 1941). In the insect there is a portion of nervous origin—the corpus cardiacum—closely associated with a portion of ectodermal origin—the corpus allatum. In the vertebrates there is a nervous rudiment—the neurohypophysis—that fuses during development with an ectodermal rudiment—the adenohypophysis. Moreover, in both the vertebrates and the insects, neurosecretory cells from the brain send their axons to the nervous portion.

WILLIER inquired what kind of cells are found in the corpus cardiacum. SCHNEIDERMAN answered that there are neurosecretory cells there, the so-called chromophil cells. In addition, there are also axon terminations of neurosecretory cells whose cell bodies lie in the brain. There are also some chromophobic cells which may play a role in secretion. The chromophobes appear to be of neuroglial origin and are thus not neurons. But the entire gland is of nervous origin. The corpus allatum is entirely different in appearance. It is an ectodermal structure

51

which arises by budding of cells between the mandibular and maxillary segments. These buds then separate from the epidermis. The prothoracic gland consists of an anastomosing network of very large cells which is richly supplied with tracheae. There are cell boundaries, but sometimes it appears almost syncytial. The cells are quite characteristic and often contain lobed nuclei of irregular shape. WILLIER then asked whether there is any evidence of a secretory cycle. SCHNEIDERMAN replied that the cells of the prothoracic gland have a secretory cycle, as do the neurosecretory cells. Where these cycles have been studied in detail, they closely parallel the morphologic events of molting. WILLIER also inquired whether the cells of the corpus allatum contain secretory granules. SCHNEIDERMAN did not know.

WILLIER then asked about the time order in which the endocrine glands of insects develop. SCHNEIDERMAN replied that this has been studied embryologically in some detail by the Japanese, who have been very interested in everything to do with the life of silkworms, and more recently by Jones (1956) in the grasshopper. The glands are all formed during embryonic life. In the case of the grasshopper, there is some information about the functional activity of these cells in embryonic life. WILLIER asked Schneiderman what he meant by "embryonic life." He stated that he means the time from fertilization until the little grasshopper hatches from the egg, i.e., the first third of life, when the legs and eyes have formed, but prior to katatrepsis, when the embryo rotates in the egg. The only endocrine structures that are evident are the neurosecretory cells. In the development of an insect like a grass-hopper, as long as the animal is inclosed within the egg and is still in the process of consuming its yolk, it can be called an "embryo." In the *Cecropia* silkworm, as long as the insect is within the egg and has not emerged, it can be called an "embryo." WILLIER then asked whether the animal emerges from the egg as a caterpillar. SCHNEIDERMAN answered in the affirmative and stated that a caterpillar is certainly no embryo. It is a highly developed, free-living organism. When the caterpillar has emerged from its egg, all the endocrine organs are fully formed. There does not appear to be an obvious postembryonic development of any of the endocrine glands of insects. They are then in their definitive condition.

KOLLROS asked whether the cells of these glands have also attained definitive size at this time. SCHNEIDERMAN stated that the cells will increase in size and in some cases in number as the animal increases in mass. WEISS asked whether anyone has gone back into the egg and fractionated development, so to speak, to see when these glands become active. SCHNEIDERMAN replied that Jones (1956) has done this. He conducted some revealing experiments on the embryonic development of grasshoppers. He showed that after the first third of embryonic life, after the embryo has acquired well-formed legs and eyes, the only endocrine organs that are evident are some large neurons in the brain destined to become neurosecretory cells. But soon after this stage, when the embryo rotates in the egg (the process called "katatrepsis") and when the most dynamic aspects of morphogenesis have been completed, the corpus allatum and the prothoracic glands appear almost simultaneously. Jones showed that if an embryo is ligated between the thorax and the abdomen just after katatrepsis, both halves continue their development perfectly normally. The only difference is that the isolated abdomen fails to undergo an embryonic molt. Cell division goes on, however, and the various embryonic structures in both halves of the ligated animal assume their definitive appearance. These experiments led to the conclusion that a good deal of embryonic morphogenesis of insects can take place without the intercession of any of the known endocrine organs. In fact, Donald Bucklin (unpublished) showed several years ago that an isolated limb of an embryonic grasshopper will continue cell division and differentiation in a hanging drop of saline in the complete absence of any endocrine structures. It appears, therefore, that the embryonic development of insects does not demand the activity of endocrine organs unless these structures are very diffuse throughout the body of the insect during embryonic life. No distinct and definitive endocrine organ is implicated in the embryonic development of insects. The role of diffuse endocrine structures remains to be seen.

WEISS inquired about the old claim of Frew (1928), who reported that the evagination of imaginal discs does not take place in larval blood but does take place in pupal blood. SCHNEIDERMAN pointed out that this, of course, involves postembryonic development. He stated that no one has ever been able to repeat Frew's experiments, although several have tried. It must have been a lucky happenstance that cells developed under the conditions of his experiments. WEISS then asked whether anyone has been able to get a result in tissue culture comparable to those of Gaillard, in which an isolated part will react to hormones. SCHNEIDERMAN answered that Loeb and Schneiderman (1956) maintained insect tissues alive for as long as $2\frac{1}{2}$ months in tissue culture, but that nothing happened. The cells merely sit there, occasionally sending out protoplasmic processes. WEISS then asked whether these cells failed even to produce a cuticle. SCHNEIDERMAN

53

stated that if they are in the midst of doing this at the time they are placed in the culture medium, they stop doing it. They are not dead, because if they are transplanted back into an insect, they develop. He feels that there are good reasons for this behavior. None of the culture media used have duplicated the proper hormonal environment. The insect's blood, strangely enough, is a highly toxic medium in which to grow insect tissues. He feels, furthermore, that it will be difficult to get any kind of true insect tissue culture until ecdysone is available. This hormone will probably prove necessary for the culture of most insect tissues. WEISS then wanted to know what evidence proves that this is a growth hormone that will act outside the body and actually make things grow that would not do so in its absence. SCHNEIDERMAN called attention to the classical experiments begun by Goldschmidt (1915), who showed that spermatocytes of the *Cecropia* silkworm isolated in hanging drops sometimes developed into sperm and sometimes failed to do so for reasons that were not understood at the time. It was subsequently shown by Schmidt and Williams (1953) that whenever the pupal insect has initiated its adult development and has quantities of PGH in its blood, spermatocytes develop into sperm when isolated in the blood. But in the blood of a pupal insect which has not begun its adult development, spermatocytes fail to differentiate. In this instance, of course, it is not a matter of growth but almost solely of differentiation under the influence of the hormone.

WEISS insisted that this was exactly his point and asked how Schneiderman could be certain that, once Karlson does get more ecdysone and it is added to the culture medium, growth will actually be stimulated. SCHNEIDERMAN could only say that it was their hope that the addition of this hormone would enable the cultures to grow. He pointed out that actually the hormone is no longer called a growth hormone. It is called "ecdysone," derived from the word *ecdysis* which means "molt." Ecdysone, then, is the molting hormone. Nevertheless, there is reasonable evidence, which has been summarized by Wigglesworth (1954), that this hormone is, in fact, a growth hormone.

· VII ·

Ontogeny of Selected Endocrine Receptors:
The Gonads and Gonoducts

The subject of the gonads and gonoducts was introduced by DR. BURNS. He stated that the effects of sex hormones on the development of the genital system have been examined in at least six species of placental mammals, as well as in the opossum, during the last 15 years. These hormones easily produce profound transformations of the sex of the genital tract but historically have had almost no effect upon the development of the gonad. This is distinctly contrary to the situation in the lower vertebrates (fishes, amphibians, and birds), in which steroid sex hormones transform the gonad quite easily. For example, if a genetic male opossum is treated with estradiol dipropionate from the age of 4 or 5 days after birth until the age of 30 days, the testes are unmodified, except that the interstitial tissue is not quite normal and patches of germinal epithelium persist here and there on the surface of the gonad. Normally, the germinal epithelium is completely lacking by this time. Moore obtained like results with opossums, and similar observations were made on treated rats by Jost and on treated mice by Raynaud (see Burns, 1950, for references and discussion). All investigators involved in this early work agreed that a testis modified to such a slight extent is essentially unmodified.

If treatment is initiated somewhat earlier, after only 2 or 3 days of postnatal life, there is more modification than before, but the gonad is still fundamentally a testis. The growth and convolution of the testicular tubules are then greatly repressed and inhibited. They remain arch-shaped tubules confined to the periphery of the gonad. Again there is a persistence of a slightly thickened germinal epithelium on the surface of the testis.

When treatment with female sex hormone is begun almost immediately after birth, the development of the tubules is greatly repressed, and the amount of interstitium is much reduced. The tunic layer—a thick fibrous layer—is very thick and swollen. The germinal epithelium persists over the entire surface of the testis (see Burns, 1956b, Figs. 11

and 12) and in places becomes 3 or 4 cells thick. It shows signs of proliferating again to form secondary sex cords (cortical cords).

If treatment with estradiol dipropionate begins immediately after birth, the effects are still more striking (see Burns, 1956*b*, Figs. 13 and 14). The testis is again greatly retarded. Tubules are beginning to degenerate. They show vacuolation in some regions of the epithelium. The tunic zone is extremely thick, and the persistent germinal epithelium is becoming quite active over the entire surface of the testis. Formation of secondary sex cords is indicated. They always originate from the germinal epithelium and thus are completely separated from the testicular part of the gonad by the wide fibrous tunic zone. There is no continuous basement membrane beneath the germinal epithelium. It is constantly interrupted and broken down wherever this kind of proliferation is occurring, i.e., wherever proliferation of secondary cords is under way. In still another specimen (Burns, 1956*b*, Figs. 17 and 18) the cortical cords are represented by great solid clusters of cells. There is no sign of germ cells in the cortex. The greatly thickened germinal epithelium is still present, but there are no germ cells in the germinal epithelium either. In such specimens the cortex may constitute two-thirds to three-quarters of the entire volume of the gland. The cortex of the normal ovary of the same age (see Burns, 1956*b*, Fig. 27) possesses cords with the same kind of configuration, but these are packed with germ cells. Actually, the germinal epithelium of the normal ovary is less well developed than in the treated embryo. In other words, the germinal epithelium of the ovotestis produced by treatment with estradiol is hypertrophic, and this is always the case. In several litters treated in this way, every male, without exception, presented this picture.

The absence of germ cells has been found to be due to the dosage of hormone used. The dosage was approximately 1 or 2 μg. of estradiol per day. This is a very low dose of hormone in comparison with dosages that have ordinarily been used in such experiments both in placental mammals and in all the earlier experiments with the opossum. Yet if the dose is cut to as little as $\frac{1}{5}$ μg. per day, germ cells appear in the cortex, as do rudimentary follicles and even follicles in which the germ cells have entered into the ovocyte stage and are beginning to grow (see Burns, 1956*b*, Figs. 22 and 23, 24 and 26). Near the center is all that is left of the original testicular structure of the gonad; the thick, whitish, non-staining material represents the tunic zone. Three litters have shown this kind of response. In some of these animals the gonads are so completely transformed that it would be difficult to convince anyone that the gonads had ever been genetic testes, were it not for the fact that there is one infallible way to demonstrate the original sex of the opossum embryo. Among all the parts of the urinogenital system, the only structures which seem to be completely unreactive to sex hormones during this entire early period of development are the scrotal sacs in the male and the pouch structures in the female (Moore, 1941; Burns, 1942). Thus a treated individual with ovaries but possessing scrotal sacs is presumably a genetic male, whereas a treated individual with ovaries but possessing pouch structures is most certainly a genetic female (see Burns, 1956*b*, Fig. 21). In both genetic males and genetic females the external genitalia are typically female and are greatly hypertrophied, as are all other parts of the female genital systems of these specimens.

Differentiation of amniote gonads is shown schematically in Figure 8. Some of the details of the diagram are still controversial. Not everyone agrees that in all mammals, or even in most mammals, primary sex cords originate quite as diagrammatically as indicated. Figure 8, *A,* represents the stage of the indifferent gonad, when primary sex cords are forming according to the classical scheme, and these represent the future tubules of the testis. At the next stage (Fig. 8, *B*) the germinal epithelium is still present; consequently, this stage is still bisexual in its potentialities. As long as the germinal epithelium is present, it is theoretically possible to stimulate a secondary proliferation of sex cords and the formation of a cortical zone (Fig. 8, *D*). As soon as the germinal epithelium disappears or becomes atrophic, as it does in normal male opossums a day or two after birth (Fig. 8, *C*), it is no longer possible to cause the transformation of the gonad into an ovary by treatment with female sex hormone. Thus the earlier experiments on opossums were initiated too late to bring about extreme modification of the gonads, whereas more recent experiments, initiated immediately after birth, produce such extreme modification. The germinal epithelium may be considered to be an endocrine receptor, since it can respond to treatment with female sex hormone by forming an ovarian cortex.

Ovaries of genetic females are also modified by the same treatment that transforms testes of genetic males (Burns, 1956*b*, Fig. 10). The ovaries are somewhat reduced in size. The cortex is not so well developed as in the normal ovary. There is the same reduction in the number of germ cells as in the testes of treated males, though in lesser degree. The fact that the number of germ cells is also reduced in treated females rules out the possibility that their reduction in treated males is due merely to the inability of a transformed testis to realize the full

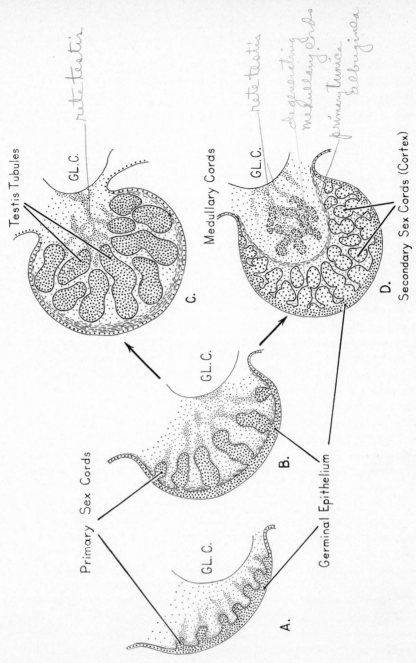

Testis Tubules

GL.C.

rete testis

Medullary Cords

GL.C.

rete testis

degenerating
medullary cords
g.
primary tunica
albuginea

C.

D.

Secondary Sex Cords (Cortex)

GL.C.

Primary Sex Cords

B.

Germinal Epithelium

GL.C.

A.

FIG. 8.—Legend on facing page

potentialities of a normal ovary. In other words, this particular defect in the gonads of transformed males is not associated with the transformation of sex per se. The germinal epithelium of the treated ovaries shows the same hypertrophy that is seen in the germinal epithelium of the transformed testes, and this is difficult to interpret. In spite of the fact that the germinal epithelium is greatly hypertrophied, the cortex itself is less developed than in a normal ovary, and there are fewer germ cells than in the normal ovary. It appears that the hormone actually interferes with the multiplication of primordial germ cells and thus reduces their number.

PRICE asked whether with a high dose of estrogen the germ cells are ever completely lacking. BURNS replied that in the same litters in which the cortex of the transformed testes is sterile, the ovarian cortex is never completely sterile, but the number of germ cells is reduced. PRICE then inquired whether there are fewer germ cells with a higher dose than with a lower one. BURNS replied that this is usually true. WEISS asked whether the nuclei are conspicuously larger in the hypertrophied germinal epithelium of treated specimens. He suggested that they might be tetraploid nuclei, i.e., that their larger size might be due to failure of cell division. BURNS replied that he had never seen any indication to suggest that the nuclei are larger than normal, although he had never scrutinized his slides with that possibility in mind. It would be necessary to measure a great many nuclei to demonstrate that point.

BURNS then commented on the fact, mentioned earlier, that the cortex of transformed testes contains a number of larger follicles containing young ovocytes, the nuclei of which distinctly show early prophase changes. Such large follicles of this character do not occur in the normal cortex of the same age. Thus along with a hypertrophy of the germinal epithelium goes the marked enlargement of a certain number of follicles in the cortex of the transformed testis. In each case there is a stimulation, direct or indirect, over and above the normal growth of these structures.

FIG. 8.—Schematic illustration of the process of sex differentiation in the gonads of amniotes, showing the various constituent tissues of the embryonic gonad and their future potentialities. To induce transformation of the testis by *estradiol dipropionate* in the opossum, it is necessary to begin treatment at the stage represented by *B*. At this stage the primary sex cords (future seminiferous tubules) have been laid down, but the germinal epithelium is still present and well preserved. In spite of the genetic male constitution, the action of the female hormone at this stage leads to preservation of the germinal epithelium and gradual degeneration of the male elements. When the latter process has reached a certain point, the germinal epithelium becomes active and behaves as in *D*. Redrawn from Burns (1955, 1956*b*).

In summary, the treatment of litters of opossums with female hormone causes the following changes in genetic males: (1) the most striking effect noted in the earlier stages of treatment is a marked retardation or inhibition of the development of the testis as a whole. The development of the testis cords is arrested. Later they undergo shrinkage and degeneration to a point where they resemble the vestigial medullary cords of the ovary. (2) The interstitial tissue is greatly repressed. The nuclei appear dense and pyknotic, and ultimately this tissue disappears entirely. (3) There is a diminution in the germ cells. These three effects are of an inhibitory or repressive character. Two effects of a positive nature have been noted: (1) the germinal epithelium in treated animals of both sexes is hypertrophic to such an extent that it greatly exceeds in thickness the germinal epithelium of normal ovaries; and (2) a certain number of young follicles in the cortex of transformed testes exhibit precocious growth. The large ovocytes in these follicles measure about 25 μ, twice the diameter of the largest follicles in normal ovaries of the same age.

PRICE asked Burns whether he visualized the inhibition of the seminiferous tubules as an indirect effect through the pituitary or as a direct effect. She suggested that the inhibition of the testicular tubules might be due to the fact that the cortex is developing and inhibiting them. BURNS stated that it is impossible to say with any certainty whether the effect of hormone treatment on the seminiferous tubules is direct or whether it is exerted through the agency of the pituitary. The simultaneous inhibition of the interstitium, which presumably eliminates production of the male hormone in the embryonic testis, could result in the persistence of the germinal epithelium and the development of the cortex. Thus development of the germinal epithelium and the cortex could be a release phenomenon due to the lack of inhibition by testicular secretion. Merely because of release from inhibition, the germinal epithelium might persist for a while and then proliferate secondary cords to form a cortex. But that does not explain the hypertrophic effect on the germinal epithelium and certain follicles which represents growth over and above normal. Something more than a simple release is involved because the germinal epithelium does not merely survive and grow to the same degree as in the normal ovary; it is exceedingly hypertrophied. In this case there is a positive stimulation, but whether it is direct or indirect in nature is unknown. The chief significance of these results is that they are the first instance in any mammal in which the histological differentiation of the gonad has been reversed experimentally. The only similar case on record is that of the freemartin, an "experiment of Nature" as Lillie called it, and that involves a transformation in the opposite direction, from an ovary into a testis.

WEISS asked, if the pituitary is involved in these sex-reversal effects, how it discriminates between male and female sex hormones. BURNS answered that, according to the classical concept of Moore and Price (1932) concerning the effects of sex hormones on the pituitary, both types of hormone, male and female, exert a depressing or inhibitory effect on the gonadotrophic functions of the pituitary. Discrimination by the pituitary between male and female hormone is not involved in his experiments, since he used only one sex hormone, namely, estrogen. If the pituitary is invoked to explain the results obtained in the experiments under discussion, the reasoning might be as follows: the hormone, by depressing the gonadotrophic function of the pituitary, prevents *indirectly* the normal growth and differentiation of the testis components—tubules and interstitium. Failure of these elements to develop permits, as a release phenomenon, the germinal epithelium to survive and ultimately to form a cortex. However, the suppression of testis differentiation is so prompt in specimens treated immediately after birth and is so extreme that *direct* action of the female hormone on the testis components must be considered. In either case, cortical development could still be regarded as a release phenomenon, except that the hypertrophic response of the germinal epithelium and the formation of precocious follicles are hardly consistent with this interpretation. All that can be said is that in the indifferent gonad and in the young developing testis both male and female sex components are present. In the testis the male component is represented by the tubular structures and by the interstitium; the female component is represented by the persisting germinal epithelium and later on by the cortical cords which it produces. It is quite clear that directly or indirectly—and at the present time no decision is possible—estradiol inhibits development of the male components and stimulates development of the female components, which, of course, is the way female hormone should act according to classical concepts.

WILLIER questioned Burns about his statement that the germinal epithelium is a female sex component. He emphasized that either the germinal epithelium can produce the covering of the testis, or it can, under the influence of female sex hormone, produce the female sex component—the cortex. He pointed out that this suggests that some sort of switch mechanism may be involved in determining the fate of the germinal epithelium. For this reason he does not consider it advisable to refer to the germinal epithelium as a female sex component. BURNS agreed that in early stages of gonad formation (Fig. 8, *A*) the germinal epithelium cannot be called a female sex component because it is producing the medullary cords, which are the testicular part of the gonad. However, experimental treatment is begun at the stage illustrated by Figure 8, *B*. At this stage the gonad is still bipotential because the testicular elements have been laid down and the germinal epithelium is still present. From this stage on, the germinal epithelium can do only the two things indicated in Figure 8, *C* and *D:* it can atrophy to form the covering membrane of the testis, or it can continue to proliferate and form a cortex. And in that sense, *at this stage of development,* the germinal epithelium, when it is present, must be regarded as a component of the gonad, which has female potentialities and never male.

KOLLROS asked whether it is possible to treat the gonad locally with female hormone. Such a treatment would eliminate the possibility of intervention by the pituitary, or at least presumably would do so. BURNS answered that this would be difficult to do for technical reasons, at least in vivo. KOLLROS then illustrated how his laboratory makes use of thyroxin pellets to produce localized effects. If such a pellet is placed just under the skin of a tadpole, an effect on the skin glands is evident (see Kollros and Kaltenbach, 1952, Fig. 5, *a*). Just above the pellet are large glands and molting of the skin. A little to one side appear very substantial glands without superficial molting. Far to the other side, only gland nests appear. The distance in the tadpole over which the local effect may be detected is perhaps 1 mm., or maybe 1.5 mm. A similar effect can be shown if the pellet is placed immediately adjacent to the area of the skin window where the front legs ordinarily emerge (see Kaltenbach, 1953*c*, Pl. 1). On the side containing the pellet there is a rupture of the window, even though the limbs are in a very embryonic condition. On the other side, which received a control pellet of cholesterol, there is no rupture; in fact, there is still a very thick opercular wall there. Because such local effects can be produced in tadpoles, the thought suggested itself that pellets of estradiol placed next to the testis might likewise have specific local effects, thereby providing one way of analyzing whether there is an influence directly on the gonad or only indirectly through the pituitary gland.

Evidence was then introduced by WILLIER which makes it seem unlikely that the pituitary is involved in transformation of the gonad. First, he commented on the fact that Wolff (1937) has demonstrated that sex reversal can be produced just as readily in pituitaryless embryos as in intact embryos. Second, he recalled that Wolff and Haffen

(1952) demonstrated that the approximation of an embryonic testis to a bit of ovarian tissue in vitro results in formation of a cortex on the testis. In this case the receptor is responding in the absence of the rest of the organism, including the anterior pituitary. SEGAL stated that sex reversal can be brought about similarly in hypophysectomized larvae of amphibians.

BURNS then suggested that the only reason for suspecting the pituitary at all is in comparison with the events after unilateral removal of an ovary in many animals. The number of maturing follicles in the remaining ovary essentially doubles under these circumstances. And if the remaining ovary is fragmented and only a portion of it is left, the number of maturing follicles in that fragment of an ovary again increases. A kind of compensatory phenomenon takes place which has been explained on the basis of gonadotrophic effects on the remaining ovary or piece of ovary. The precocious growth of a few follicles in the testicular cortex is essentially the same kind of compensation as that which occurs after partial ovariectomy in mammals. He then stated that the question of the intervention of the pituitary in any differential way in sexual differentiation has scarcely been raised. It seems to have no importance except that it may influence quantitatively the growth of structures later on. It is not qualitatively involved in the phenomena of sex differentiation. WEISS was anxious to have this point emphasized for the record.

PRICE then inquired whether estrogen treatment stops migration of germ cells from the extra-gonadal areas. BURNS answered that this possibility has not been explored. He stated that nothing is known about the primordial germ cells of the opossum before they are in the gonad. Whether the sterility of the cortex in the earlier experiments could be attributed to an early arrest of germ cell movement seems doubtful, since the testicular part of these gonads is not sterile. WILLIER inquired whether the germ cells of the opossum are already in the germinal epithelium at the earliest normal stages examined. BURNS answered that they are in the gonad but not in the germinal epithelium. They are always beneath the germinal epithelium in the stromal part of the gonad. He has seen no evidence that they come from the germinal epithelium, although his observations are not conclusive on this point.

MARTINOVITCH then asked Burns whether his interpretation of the action of the hormone on the germ cell tract is that the hormone may inhibit cellular division. BURNS replied that this is all he can think of. The number of germ cells is greatly reduced. It is reduced in both the testis and the ovary. The only treatment has been the administration of the female hormone. Consequently, this hormone must, in some way, be responsible for the reduction. Martinovitch then asked whether there is any evidence of the possibility that the hormone may exert a direct injury effect on the germ cells. Burns answered that this might be the explanation, although he knows of no other evidence to show that excessive hormone directly injures germ cells. The reduction in number of germ cells appears to occur before the spermatocyte or the oöcyte stages. It is the number of gonia that is reduced. Thus, whatever the effect of the hormone, it is exerted very early.

Weiss then inquired whether treatment at the same stage with a whole range of dosages of testosterone from zero to shock doses would give the same effect. Burns answered that he did not know, since up to now there are no experiments in which testosterone was given at the early stages at which an effect on the germ cells is noted. Kollros suggested that the switch mechanism, insofar as the germinal epithelium is concerned, i.e., whether it will form cortex of the female type or simply the covering of the testis, may be a *direct* effect of the hormone treatment, whereas the number of germ cells produced may be influenced *indirectly* through the pituitary. Weiss considered this to be an oversimplification of the situation. He suggested that the pituitary may somehow be involved by setting the level of the response of the gonad tissue without determining which direction it will take; the chemical configuration of the hormone administered may actually determine the direction of development of the receptor. Burns took this occasion to emphasize that an analysis of the way in which the female hormone produces its effects would require an almost unlimited number of experiments. This would be exceedingly difficult with opossums because it is extremely difficult to obtain litters young enough to produce the transformation of the testis. The number of litters born at a stage when the germinal epithelium is still present is only a very small proportion of the total litters available. Thus there is considerable variation in the condition of the gonads at the moment young opossums are born. The experimenter must always wait for litters in just the right stage of development at the time of birth, and this means that studies of this type cannot progress as rapidly as desirable.

Dr. Willier called attention to the gonoducts as endocrine receptors and asked Burns to comment briefly on the effect of sex hormones on the various sex ducts. Is the hormone selective in its action on the sex ducts? Is this effect direct or indirect? If the testis is caused to transform into an ovary or into an ovotestis, are there simultaneous changes in the female direction in the gonoducts? Burns stated that this is a rather old story which has been in the literature for many years. The situation in the opossum does not differ significantly from that in half-a-dozen other mammals in which the mother has been treated with hormone during pregnancy. The genital tracts of the young are rather completely transformed in many cases. In general, the effects of the hormones are fairly specific. Female hormones stimulate development of Müllerian ducts and inhibit Wolffian ducts, and vice versa. An exception to this last statement must be made in the case of the mammals, in which testosterone and its compounds do not inhibit the Müllerian ducts except partially in one or two species; Burns (1955) should be consulted for details. In the opossum, for example, only the vaginal part of the Müllerian duct is suppressed. Opossums which received estradiol treatment possess greatly hypertrophied external genital structures of the female type. Estradiol completely inhibits development of the prostates in young treated males. All derivatives of the Müllerian ducts are greatly hypertrophied in both sexes following treatment with estradiol, whereas the Wolffian ducts are unmodified and appear as in controls. The hormones appear to be acting directly on the individual primordia, and the effects are specific if care is taken to control the dosage. Paradoxical effects are encountered with exceedingly large dosages, especially with androgens, which, in higher concentrations, stimulate Müllerian duct derivatives. Lower dosages do not cause such paradoxical effects. WILLIER emphasized that such results indicate that there are latent differences in response based on pre-existing heterogeneity. The sex ducts respond in a differential manner to male or female sex hormones, depending on their inherent constitution.

MÜHLBOCK then presented some of his experiments on granulosa-cell tumors in mice which show how sensitive the cells are to different dosages of hormones (Van Nie and Mühlbock, 1956). He stated that, after transplantation, most granulosa-cell tumors grow better in males than in females. In orchidectomized males the rate of growth decreases to the level of growth in females. The castration effect in males can be prevented by androgenic hormones. It is striking that estrogens and progesterone exert the same accelerating effect as do androgens on the growth of these tumors. A more detailed study by Van Nie (1957) demonstrated that some of these tumors grow only at a very distinct hormone level (Fig. 9). With low doses, as with very high doses, the growth of the tumors is not optimal. Discontinuation of hormone application causes a very remarkable regression of the tumors. It is striking that after transplantation the tumor cells may lie dormant in the subcutaneous tissue for a long time and only begin to grow after stimula-

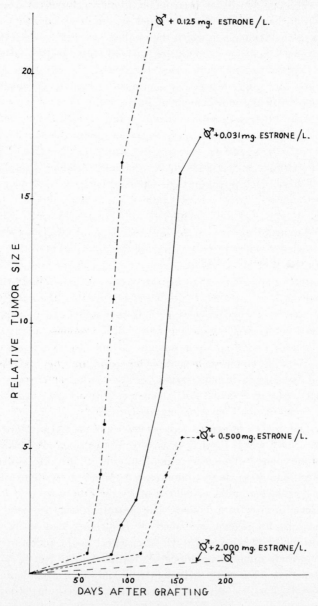

Fig. 9.—Influence of different doses of estrone in drinking water on the growth of a transplanted ovarian tumor. Redrawn from Van Nie (1957).

tion with hormones. Moreover, if the tumor undergoes a certain morphologic change, it is no longer dependent on the hormone. It somehow or other loses its ability to respond selectively. It can no longer be suppressed with high dosages of the hormone. This effect is independent of the pituitary gland, since the same results are obtained when the experiments are performed on hypophysectomized animals. SCHNEIDERMAN asked whether the tumor had lost the ability to respond or whether it had gained the ability to be independent. When a cell differentiates, it certainly loses the ability to produce certain substances and, in the process, gains nutritional requirements. WEISS put it this way: If hydrogen and chlorine are combined to form hydrochloric acid, they lose the properties of the hydrogen and the chlorine, but they gain the properties of the acid!

SEGAL next presented an example of Nature's experiment in sex reversal in the mammalian gonad. He illustrated a testicular biopsy which was taken from a human genetic female as proved by the sex-chromatin test (Segal and Nelson, 1957). This genetic female developed infertile testes and the complete secondary sex apparatus of a male. This case and all others of this so-called Klinefelter syndrome involve individuals who are raised as men and who frequently marry as males. In some cases spermatogenesis is complete in some tubules. This condition must certainly have an embryonic origin, with the indifferent embryonic gonad differentiating in a direction opposite from its genetic constitution. The normally dominant embryonic gonadal cortex of this genetic female has been suppressed in favor of the development of the medulla.

WILLIER then reviewed experiments performed in his laboratory much earlier, involving administration of sex hormones to chick embryos (Willier, 1939, 1942). In genetic males there is an incipient ovarian cortex on the left gonad which is usually lacking on the right side, although occasionally a little bit of ovarian cortex is present on the right side also. As long as this incipient ovarian cortex is present when introduction of female hormone occurs, it can respond by developing into a beautiful and typical ovarian cortex. The two sides of the body differ with respect to the time that the incipient cortex disappears. If differentiation proceeds in the male direction, the primary sex cords become the seminiferous tubules, and certain ducts persist to become passageways for escape of spermatozoa. The Müllerian ducts disappear. If differentiation proceeds in the female direction, an ovarian cortex forms on the left side. The primary sex cords remain on the left, but they assume a different form than they do in the male: they hollow out instead

67

of remaining solid. The oviduct develops from the Müllerian duct on the left side only; it disappears on the right side, with the exception of a small rudiment. Thus the embryo has a bisexual organization, at first, with both male and female components, just as in the mammal.

Sex differentiation can be modified by the introduction of sex hormones. Even though the dosage is carefully controlled, it is impossible to determine the exact dosage actually reaching the embryo; hence the results are somewhat variable. If female sex hormone is added to genetic males, the left testis is altered in form and structure; it becomes a flattened, ovary-like body consisting of both ovarian and testicular tissue (ovotestis). In extreme cases it is practically indistinguishable from a normal left ovary (see Willier, 1939, Figs. 28 and 31). Near the hilus is typical testicular tissue. More centrally located is medullary tissue, but the sex cords in this location are hollowed out to form the female pattern of the male sex component. A thick ovarian cortex occurs at the surface and contains many germ cells. If female sex hormone is administered after the ninth day, when the incipient ovarian cortex has disappeared, no reversal effects can be obtained. In such experiments the original sex of the treated embryo can be determined because the fertile eggs come from a cross between two breeds of chickens in which all the male chicks have a patch of white feathers on the top of the head, whereas the female chicks have black plumage over the head. These plumage characteristics are independent of sex hormones. The right testis of treated males remains unchanged except in those cases exhibiting complete or nearly complete reversal of the left testis; then it is reduced in size, flattened, and contains ovarian medullary tissue; its testicular nature is never lost. The Müllerian ducts persist on both sides, either partially or completely, depending on the dosages given. With very large dosages they become hypertrophied. There is no effect on the Wolffian ducts. In the normal male the testes are cylindrical in outline, and the Müllerian ducts are absent (see Willier, 1939, Fig. 29).

If male sex hormone is added to genetic females, the form and structure of the ovaries are altered (Willier, 1939, Figs. 30 and 33). Each ovary, and especially the right, assumes the form of a testis. The ovarian cortex on the left gonad thins out and degenerates, while the ovarian medulla hypertrophies and transforms into testicular tissue at the hilus. The medulla of the right ovary hypertrophies and transforms into testicular sex cords. It is much more difficult to bring about the reversal of the sex components of the female gonad than of the male gonad. Oviducts exhibit various grades of retrogressive changes, the left one often undergoing reduction to a short rudimentary portion containing a lumen.

The Wolffian ducts and certain mesonephric tubules which begin to hypertrophy with low dosages become enormously swollen when 1 mg. or more of hormone is given. Thus in these experiments the receptors respond to sex hormones selectively. Male components respond to male hormone, whether they are present in genetic males or in genetic females, and female components respond to female hormone, whether they are present in genetic males or in genetic females. Thus, as in the case of mammals, there are latent differences in response based on pre-existing heterogeneity. The sex components are already tuned, so to speak, to respond to a specific kind of hormone. The same kinds of changes can be brought about by injections of sex hormones into duck embryos.

Domm (1939) and others have shown that when the left ovary of a young bird is removed after hatching, the right ovary, which is potentially a testis, actually transforms into a testis. Similarly, the left ovarian medulla transforms into a testis after removal of its cortex. Thus the ovarian cortex seems to be exerting an inhibitory effect on the expression of the male components of the ovary. WEISS asked in connection with what had been said earlier about differences in heterozygous and homozygous sexes in birds, as compared with mammals, whether there is any evidence in mammals that the *male* component of the gonads exerts an inhibitory influence on the cortical component. In other words, is the situation just the opposite from that found in birds? SEGAL stated that the case of human sex reversal in the Klinefelter syndrome, presented earlier, illustrates exactly this condition. The embryological aspects of this situation have been completely discussed in recent papers by Segal and Nelson (1957) and by Witschi, Nelson, and Segal (1957). BURNS stated that in the opossum there is no experimental evidence on this point as yet, although, as he mentioned earlier, it is possible to explain the development of the cortex on the transformed testes of opossums treated with female sex hormone in terms of a release from an inhibition normally exercised by the medullary component. WILLIER stated that the freemartin might be a case of this sort because the left ovarian cortex failed to develop in most of Lillie's cases. Bissonnette (1924), however, had some cases in which there was a little ovarian cortex present. Under these circumstances an ovotestis was produced. Whether an incipient ovarian cortex is present in cattle has not been demonstrated; however, an incipient ovarian cortex has been demonstrated in certain mammals, like the cat. BURNS emphasized that the germinal epithelium itself at a certain stage represents an incipient cortex, i.e., during the indifferent stage of the gonad. WEISS inquired whether anyone has transplanted a young male gonad into the early cortex of an ovary to see whether there is a local inhibitory effect. BURNS replied that it would be very difficult to do technically but that doubtless a clever operator like Dr. Jost could do the operation. WILLIER added that Wolff has been able in some of his experiments to produce an ovarian cortex on the right ovary, provided that the treatment begins early enough. Typically the right ovary lacks an ovarian cortex, but occasionally little patches of ovarian cortex are present on the right gonad, and these can then respond to treatment with female sex hormones.

PRICE inquired whether there is any explanation of the asymmetry in the avian reproductive system. WILLIER replied that this is but part of the fundamental asymmetry of the chick embryo. Even in earlier stages, i.e., in primitive streak and head process stages, there are differences in the capacity of the two sides of the body to produce an organ such as the eye in isolates transplanted to the chorio-allantoic membrane. If the transverse eye-forming region is cut into three pieces (right, median, and left), the capacity of the right piece for formation of an eye is lower than the capacity of the left piece. The median piece is more or less intermediate between the two lateral pieces. In the case of every organ-forming system that has been examined, there is a greater tendency to produce more tissue, and more normal tissue, in grafts of pieces taken from the left side of the body. WEISS mentioned that the same thing is true of amphibians and sea urchins. WILLIER suggested that we may be wrong in teaching students that organisms are bilaterally symmetrical; actually, they are bilaterally asymmetrical. WEISS commented that all this really amounts to is that one side of the body is ahead of the other; it gets a head start in development and thus is a little older than the other half. BURNS also mentioned the fact that there is an asymmetry in the adult organism that is not confined to the reproductive tract. For example, the aortic arch in birds is on the right side and not on the left, as in mammals, and there are other very marked asymmetries in the adult.

In relation to this topic of asymmetry, GAILLARD next commented briefly on some differences in the behavior of explants derived from the right and left ovaries of man. When organ cultures of the peripheral part of the cortex (including the germinal epithelium) are made from the ovaries taken from a $3\frac{1}{2}$-month human fetus, the explants taken from the right ovary begin to degenerate after some days. Complete disorganization of the typical ovarian structure occurs, and within 1 week it is hardly possible to recognize the tissue as a derivative of the ovary; complete degeneration may occur. By contrast, there is a complete regeneration in explants taken from the left ovary, and especially in cultures made from its caudal pole. Cordlike proliferations develop, in which numerous oögonia and oöcytes in all stages of meiotic prophase are to be seen. Such differential behavior of explants taken from left and right ovaries also exists when donors are 4-, 5-, or 6-month fetuses. These observations seem to indicate some kind of inequality in the regenerative capacities of organ fragments isolated from the two sides of the body. PRICE inquired how many explants were involved. GAILLARD answered approximately 45 of each.

WILLIER then pointed out in this connection that there is evidence that in monotremes the left ovary is the one that produces the eggs. Furthermore, in the case of the freemartin, the changes differ on the right and left sides. BURNS commented that he had not noticed distinct lateral differences between the two sides in the reaction of sex primordia in the opossum but that he was not prepared to state that differences of this nature would not be found if precise measurements were made. Certainly, if they exist, they are not so conspicuous as in birds. SCHOTTÉ then asked whether there is any evidence that ovarian tumors occur more frequently on the left than on the right side in humans. MÜHLBOCK replied that in their experiments they often see a tumor on one side only, but that there is no difference in frequency between left and right sides.

WEISS then stated that it was his feeling that a point had been reached in the discussion where special attention should be given to the factors involved in the establishment of the latent differences in response of the receptors. Development begins, of course, with a zygote, which is genetically male or genetically female, and, as development progresses, various embryonic rudiments arise whose cells are all genetically male or genetically female. When hormones are added to the developing system, either from the outside (exogenous hormones) or from the inside (endogenous hormones), genetically male rudiments respond differently, at least quantitatively, from genetically female rudiments. He raised several questions about the progress of development of the rudiments. Do they develop as completely closed systems up to the moment when they are suddenly confronted with hormones for the first time? And when they are first exposed to hormones, are they then changed in some way once and for all, such that they are not influenced in any way thereafter by the presence of these hormones? The original difference in genetic composition of zygotic males and zygotic females may be detectable in early stages by differences in sex chromatin, in the nucleolus, etc. But the different reactions of receptors of zygotic males and zygotic females

71

must be conditioned by much more than the original genetic differences of the cells present in the receptors. The cells of each receptor as they develop are surrounded and influenced by a male or a female environment consisting of neighboring male or female cells and their products. It is well known from experimental embryology that many cellular interactions play back and forth in a complex fashion between the various organ rudiments derived from the zygote. The reactions between the organ rudiments of a male zygote ought to be somewhat different from the reactions between the organ rudiments of a female zygote, whether we can detect them or not. When the establishment of heterogeneity in receptors is discussed, what should be considered is the sum total not only of the initial differences in genetic composition but of all the different interactions within male and female individuals that take place during their developmental history. If this is true, then the underlying conditions for quantitatively different reactions of male and female rudiments to the same hormonal conditions originate progressively with time. During development of the pituitary glands of genetic males and genetic females there is probably never a stage when the cells are exactly identical in the two sexes in their response to hormones. They are different when they begin to develop, but they also respond differently to influences from adjacent organs as they develop, and thus they become increasingly different from one another in a progressive way. Whether reactive capacities are established progressively in this way needs to be tested, and, unless the problems are posed in this form, they will not be tested. When something is added from the outside—for example, an exogenous hormone—it does not act from scratch; it does not operate on a system which has no history and has just been waiting unchanged for testosterone or stilbestrol or what not to be added. Whatever is done experimentally to the organism has to be rated against the background of the previous history of the reacting embryonic structures, and this history has not been immune from tissue interactions. Instead of talking about an exclusive monopoly of a particular glandular discharge in the regulation of an otherwise indifferent and ignorant system, the possibility should be considered that innumerable agents of similar nature have been acting on that system throughout its developmental history, although in a less dramatic way. Thus the inherent characteristics of a later stage are more than the genetic constitution received by the zygote; they are the products of a historical course of interactions between the original genome and its environment. It is rare, rather than common, that such sharply defined reaction times are encountered as those characteristic of the phenomena of metamorphosis.

It is absurd, therefore, to inquire whether a particular response is determined hormonally or genetically. Even if it appears superficially to be determined hormonally, the hormone source is determined by the genome plus the embryonic history that is behind it when its product is first encountered. Hormone action is probably not a one-shot operation; the agent involved more likely operates at different times, repeatedly, producing different results, depending on the time at which it works. It may change a given system in a given way at one moment, but it likely exerts its effects again and again on the system as time goes on.

SCHNEIDERMAN commented that it is probably the precipitousness of things like metamorphosis that causes us to think too much of the triggering action of hormones rather than of a sustained and repetitive action at different stages of maturity. He mentioned that in the case of metamorphosis of insects it makes a great deal of difference whether a big dose of hormone is given at one time or whether a little bit is given over a long time; quite different types of organisms are produced. BURNS pointed out that, at various points along any given chain of interactions that is involved in the development of any receptor, some of its final characteristics can be influenced with hormones, but others cannot. The system is in constant transformation. But BURNS also emphasized that, at given moments in development, certain irreversible changes can and do occur almost instantaneously, perhaps not in a matter of minutes, or even of hours, but within a relatively short span of time. He recalled the situation in the opossum testis which he had discussed earlier and illustrated a section in which the germinal epithelium on the surface of the testis had separated from the primary sex cords (see Burns, 1956*b*, Fig. 5). He emphasized that this is about 24 hours after the stage at which hormone injections were made. By this stage it is quite impossible to restore any activity of the germinal epithelium. Thus within 24 hours the germinal epithelium has lost its capacity to respond to estrogen, and no treatment will cause any further development of the cortex or even any hypertrophy of the germinal epithelium. WILLIER stated that the same thing is true of the left testis of the chick. It rather suddenly reaches a stage where it is no longer responsive. BURNS suggested that there is a similar critical period for the prostatic buds, although perhaps not so brief. WEISS stated that he wished only to emphasize that the developing system loses what it does as a result of the environment it has been exposed to during its development prior to that time, rather than exclusively as the result of an innate change of its own.

SEGAL then reported on the work and interpretations of Chang (Chang, 1955; Chang and Witschi, 1955*b*) which provide an example of the concept developed by Weiss, namely, that an organ system reacts in accordance with and as a result of its entire past history, including its genotype. In *Xenopus* the male is homozygous (XX), whereas the female is heterozygous (XY). Estrogen added to the aquarium water containing *Xenopus* larvae causes feminization of genetic males. Androgens have no effect on genetic females. Thus in the latter case a zygote starting with the XY chromosome composition undergoes a developmental history which precludes a possible interference with sex differentiation by the administration of androgens. XX females produced by the treatment of genetic males with estrogen can be mated with normal XX males. The result of such a cross is obviously 100 per cent larvae of the XX genotype, i.e., genetic males. If, during the third week in development, such larvae are treated for a 3-day period with estrogens, they can be sex-reversed to XX females and could later be used in matings as functional females. If, however, following this short but feminizing treatment with estrogens, these larvae are subjected to the administration of androgen, the resultant gonad is of the testicular type. In other words, it is possible to bring about an androgen-induced masculinization of the gonad of *Xenopus* larvae if the ovary-bearing larva is of the *homozygous* genotype. If it is of the *heterozygous* type, as under normal circumstances, androgen has no such effect. This difference in original genotype results in a different potentiality in the receptor organ to respond to the hormonal stimulus. In *Rana* the homozygous female can be masculinized with androgens. In *Ambystoma* the heterozygous female, like *Xenopus*, cannot be sex-reversed with androgens. Such observations led Chang to postulate that there exists a possible relationship between female homozygosity and a positive masculinizing influence of androgen. Thus the genetic background is carried through the lives of these animals, and it takes an ingenious experimental design to bring it out. WEISS then inquired whether it is generally true that the homozygous sex has the greater inertia, so to speak. BURNS answered that, as far as castration experiments in birds and mammals are concerned, the castrate type in birds closely resembles the normal male (XX), whereas the castrate type in mammals closely resembles the normal female (XX). In *Xenopus*, according to Schotté, the castrate closely resembles the female (XY).

SCHNEIDERMAN then pointed out that insects have no sex hormones, as far as is known. The insect sex organs are sex-limited from the earliest stages of their development and cannot be modified by transplantation. WEISS stated that all that can be said from such experiments is that if sex hormones exist in insects, the same ones are present in both males and females. Even though they do not come from the ovaries and testes and even though removal of the gonads and cross-transplantation experiments have no effect at all, this does not mean that they are not produced at other sites.

MÜHLBOCK then asked whether anything is known about the influence of the age of the parents on the development of the young in mammals. He stated that he has some evidence that the age of the mother exerts an influence on the development of tumors in mice (Mühlbock, 1956). WEISS referred him to the conference on the prenatal influences in mammalian development that had already been held.

· VIII ·

Conditioning Effects on End Organs

According to WEISS, conditioning is a non-overt act; it is an action on an organic system that leaves a residue which is not immediately detectable. Any subsequent action will have been modified by the previous activity of the so-called conditioning agent. In the case of a nerve, conditioning changes the excitatory state or the threshold of the system. This results in an expressed or overt action when another factor (stimulus) is introduced at a lower or higher dose or for a longer or shorter exposure.

TONUTTI then illustrated the conditioning effect of hormones on the destructive action of bacterial toxins against tissues (Tonutti, 1953). It is well known that diphtheria toxin causes practically complete destruction of the adrenal gland within 24 hours if administered at a dose of 5 M.L.D. The organ loses its yellow color and becomes cherry-red. Histologic examination reveals a severe hemorrhagic reaction and severe necrosis. In the hypophysectomized guinea pig the adrenal remains yellow after inoculation with the same dose of diphtheria toxin; histologically, there is no vascular reaction and no necrosis. Hypophysectomy therefore completely protects the adrenal tissue against the destructive action of diphtheria toxin, or, in other words, adrenal tissue loses its responsiveness to diphtheria toxin after hypophysectomy. If hypophysectomized guinea pigs are treated with ACTH and are then injected with diphtheria toxin, the responsiveness of the adrenal tissue to the toxin reappears. This seems to be definite proof that the destructive action of diphtheria toxin on the adrenal is conditioned by ACTH.

In the normal animal, diphtheria toxin has two actions: (1) a non-specific action which results in the release of ACTH by the pituitary, as a result of which there is a physiologic stimulation of the adrenal by ACTH, and (2) a specific action which leads to bleeding and necrosis in the adrenal, but only if the adrenal tissue is stimulated by ACTH. The non-specific action can be separated from the specific tissue-damaging effect of the toxin by the following experiment. If diphtheria toxin is injected into the brain of animals previously immunized by intraperitoneal administration of diphtheria antitoxin, the animals die from diphtheria intoxication. But in the periphery of the body the toxin is neutralized. Under the conditions of this experiment the adrenal cortex shows only the physiologic signs of ACTH stimulation (increased number of mitoses, increased nuclear volume in all three zones, and the so-called progressive transformation), but no hemorrhage and no necrosis.

Diphtheria toxin is distributed over the entire body after injection. But normally other organs, such as the ovaries and the testes, do not respond even to very high doses of the toxin. However, pretreatment of infant animals with gonadotrophins followed by the injection of only 2 M.L.D. of the toxin results in a very pronounced hemorrhagic necrosis of the ovaries or the testes. Even more instructive is the observation that hypophysectomized and castrated female guinea pigs previously treated with estradiol show, after administration of diphtheria toxin, a severe hemorrhagic necrosis of the endometrium, but no lesions of the adrenal cortex. Without treatment with estradiol, even very high doses of the toxin are ineffective on the mucosa of the uterus.

The specific action of other kinds of bacterial toxins differs from that of diphtheria toxin. As far as their effect on the adrenal cortex is concerned, three types of bacterial products can be recognized (Table 2): (1) Botulinus toxin acts on the adrenal gland only as other stressors do. Its effect on the adrenals is purely non-specific. There is no specific tissue-damaging action. Therefore, the adrenal shows no destructive lesions. (2) Diphtheria toxin possesses a tissue-damaging action that is strictly related to the stimulation of the adrenals by ACTH. (3) Meningococcal toxin gives two kinds of action: (*a*) a non-specific action, resulting in release of ACTH by the pituitary, and (*b*) a specific tissue-damaging effect, which, contrary to the diphtheria toxin, is not principally related to stimulation of the gland by ACTH. Hemorrhage and necrosis occur even in the absence of the pituitary. For details, consult Tonutti (1953, 1956).

WEISS inquired whether the action of hypophysectomy is due to the fact that excitability of the tissues normally increases in the absence of the pituitary. He suggested that it might also be due to the fact that removal of the hypophysis brings other endocrine organs into compensatory operation. TONUTTI answered that it is the absence of ACTH per se which is responsible because normal behavior of the tissue can be completely restored by substitution with ACTH. The gonads, adrenals, and thyroids are inactive after hypophysectomy. No other glands have a similar action. WEISS then inquired whether diphtheria toxin has an

77

effect on mitotic activity. Tonutti answered that when bleeding occurs in the adrenal gland after treatment of the animal with diphtheria toxin, mitosis stops immediately. There are no mitoses in any animal in which the adrenal is hemorrhagic unless there are only small spots of hemorrhagic necrosis. If the destructive action of the toxin is absent, there are great numbers of mitoses.

TABLE 2*

EFFECTS OF THREE TYPES OF BACTERIAL TOXINS
ON THE ADRENAL CORTEX

			Non-specific "Stress" Action on Adrenals		Specific Nocuous Action on Adrenal Tissue	
			Depletion of Cholesterol Esters	Morpho-kinetic Action	Hemor-rhage	Necrosis
I	Botulinus toxin	Normal	||||||	||||||		
		Hypophysec-tomized				
II	Diphtheria toxin	Normal	||||||	||||||	||||||	||||||
		Hypophysec-tomized				
III	Coli lipopoly-saccharide or meningo-coccal toxin	Normal	||||||	||||||	||||||	||||||
		Hypophysec-tomized			||||||	||||||

* Blank = negative; ruled = positive. From Tonutti (1953).

Weiss then asked whether there is any information about the point of attack of ACTH in this case. What does it sensitize? Does the endothelium of the capillaries become fragile, or what does happen? Tonutti answered that the ACTH acts on all components of the adrenal cortexes: capillary walls, interstitial tissue, and parenchymal cells. He considers the adrenal tissue to respond as a whole. Weiss expanded his question into a discussion. He inquired to what extent this is always true of composite organs where there is always an epithelial component, a stroma, and a vascular bed, in addition to nerves. Does the stroma or the vascular bed react selectively? He recalled that the earlier discussion of embryological phenomena placed increased emphasis on the specificity of action of the stromal component of organs. TONUTTI stated that usually the capillaries in normal adrenals are not very large and are not readily seen; after treatment with diphtheria toxin they become very much enlarged. They suffer stasis, and some exudation takes place. WEISS suggested that the occurrence of stasis suggests the existence of a local constriction somewhere. The capillary bed has clamped down. Thus there must be an action on the capillary wall. WILLIER agreed that this is probably so because the capillary wall of the adrenal gland is no doubt different from the capillary wall of any other endocrine gland and consequently can react in a selective way. It is likely that the capillary part of each organ assumes gradually during its development the same type of specificity as the other components of that organ. TONUTTI then pointed out that there is even selectivity within the adrenal in this respect. The capillaries of the medulla of normal animals react against diphtheria toxin even earlier than those of the cortex. In the hypophysectomized animals the capillary reaction is restricted sharply to the capillaries of the medulla. WILLIER then inquired concerning the direction of blood flow in the adrenal. TONUTTI answered that it flows from the capsule to the medulla. He also emphasized that it is astonishing that the medullary capillaries, which are continuations of the capillaries of the cortex, react after hypophysectomy, whereas the latter do not. The two sets of capillaries must be different in their reactive capacities.

WEISS then asked about the vascular reaction of the comb of the fowl to hormone treatment. WILLIER indicated that it is a similar story, except that a mucoid type of connective tissue is involved. WEISS then asked whether in this case the primary reaction to the hormone treatment is in the capillary bed or in the mucoid tissue. TONUTTI stated that it is in the capillaries. This means that the primary reaction is the dilatation of the capillaries and the secondary reaction is a deposition of ground substance. He also pointed out another fine example, namely, the sexual skin of the baboon (Bachman, Collip, and Selye, 1936). This is an end organ for estradiol. When it is transplanted to another region of the body, the transplanted sexual skin also becomes red. But flank skin transplanted to the sex region of the baboon remains pale.

PRICE then inquired whether ACTH acts directly on the walls of the capillaries or whether it simply stimulates production of corticoids which affect the capillary wall. The hemorrhage might well result from the effects of the cortisone produced in response to ACTH. TONUTTI answered that this is not the case. If animals are prepared with cortisone for 3 weeks, causing suppression of ACTH secretion, the adrenals fail to react, just as in the case of hypophysectomy. Thus cortisone cannot be the conditioning factor for the lesion of the capillaries following treatment with the toxin.

WEISS returned the discussion to the experiments involving baboon skin. Where do the capillaries of the transplanted skin come from? If they arise from the local area where the graft is placed, they must have acquired their specific response from the transplanted epithelial component. But is it not equally possible that the capillary bed is brought along with the transplant? GAILLARD mentioned that in the work of Merwin and Algire (1956) the capillaries sprout out from both the graft and the host. WEISS agreed and stated that he believes that a lot of the incompatibility reactions between graft and host are due to the incompatibility of the two types of vessels in the vascular mosaic. Some of the terminal roots of the blood vessels come from the graft. MARTINO-VITCH mentioned that in heterotransplants (rat to cat) it is only the vessels of capillary size that enter the transplant. He never observed a vessel of the size of an artery or vein to penetrate the graft (Martino-vitch, 1956). In homotransplants of the rat adrenal gland a secondary inner capsule appears if the host is hypophysectomized. If the hosts are then treated with ACTH, the secondary capsule disappears as the cortex begins to regenerate; apparently the tissue of the capsule is used up in building new vessels (Martinovitch, 1955). WEISS then stated that, even if the capillaries come from the transplant, they still have to acquire their specificity earlier in ontogeny as part of mosaic formation.

MARTINOVITCH then inquired whether Dr. Tonutti had ever seen the collapse of blood vessels in the adrenal following hypophysectomy. TONUTTI replied that the whole adrenal shrinks. MARTINOVITCH mentioned that hemorrhages are a fairly common occurrence in ocular adrenal grafts. They are usually followed by a reduction in the size of the graft, which may indicate the obliteration of some of the vessels. WEISS asked Martinovitch whether the point he was trying to make is that even simple hypophysectomy can cause a partial collapse, which would then be accentuated by diphtheria toxin. However, TONUTTI again emphasized that there is no reaction in the hypophysectomized animal. MARTINOVITCH added that extravasation preceded by disten-tion often takes place in grafts following hypophysectomy of the host. The fact that the inner capsule comes into sight after hypophysectomy and then disappears after ACTH is added to the hypophysectomized host indicates that some of the vessels undergo degeneration at the time of hypophysectomy, just as they do in vitro. TONUTTI stated that the whole inner layer of the adrenal undergoes involution after hypophysectomy and that, of course, the capillaries of this region degenerate.

WEISS summarized the discussion by stating that (*a*) some of the hormonal effects are not directly visible but provide fluctuating backgrounds against which each individual agent must be rated, and (*b*) the point of attack of these may be not only on the specific glandular tissue or the most conspicuous part of the organ but on the capillary network as well.

He then asked what is known about the stroma of an organ in any response situation. The stroma does change, but does it do so in an unspecific way? Is it simply the result of the alterations of the specific epithelial tissues and/or vascular tissues, or is the stroma itself differently disposed in different parts of the body in its response to hormonal influences? SEGAL called attention to the effects of estrogen on the prostates. Some investigators have reported that it is the increase in the stromal component of the rat prostate after estrogen treatment that actually causes an increase in the weight of the gland. The weight of the gland decreases in pituitaryless rats and then increases following administration of estrogen. Histologic examination shows this increase to be in the stroma and not in the glandular elements of the prostate. Burns suggested that the reaction of the stromal tissues is not limited to the prostate. The connective tissues and sheaths of the entire reproductive tract show this kind of hypertrophy in the presence of estrogen. The greatly swollen external genitalia of the young opossums treated with estrogen are due to the reaction of the stromal elements. The sheath around the sinus and around the erectile bodies is enormously hypertrophied in the presence of estrogen. The connective tissue of the uterine wall reacts in the same way, and, of course, you get the same reaction in the prostate because the prostate stroma is derived from the sheath of the sinus. SEGAL emphasized that in the same animal in which a proliferation of the stroma of the urogenital system occurs there is no parallel proliferation of the subcutaneous stromal elements. WEISS inquired whether the response of subcutaneous connective tissue in endocrine obesity is a case in point. This would be a localized response to hormonal imbalance.

GAILLARD reviewed experiments involving organ culture. Slices of the uterus of 3-week-old mice provided with 0.005 I.U. of estrone undergo proliferation exclusively in the connective tissue of the endometrium; the addition of 0.050 I.U. of estrone leads to a proliferation of smooth-muscle cells. If so-called pure strains of periosteal fibroblasts and of heart fibroblasts are cultured and are treated with crystalline growth hormone, the heart fibroblasts react optimally, with mitosis at a concentration of one in ten thousand, whereas the periosteal fibroblasts react optimally at a concentration of one in three million. If periosteal fibroblasts are derived from another and younger embryo, still another dosage is needed to obtain an optimal reaction with mitosis. These results suggest that fibrocytic elements from different sources and from animals at different ages can have different sensitivities or can change their sensitivity toward growth hormone.

WILLIER raised a question as to whether estrogen exerts a conditioning effect on the uterus preparatory to the action of some other hormone such as progesterone. SEGAL answered that this has been worked out very carefully in the rabbit by McPhail (1934), who showed that progesterone has no proliferative effect on the endometrium unless it is preceded by a priming dose of estrogen. BURNS cited the mammary gland as another example of this relationship. The immature mammary gland of the rabbit will not respond to prolactin and secrete milk until it is first conditioned with estrogen. Another example can be cited from the amphibians. The gonads of *Rana catesbiana,* a species which has a very long larval life lasting into the second year, undergo sexual differentiation into ovary and testis rather early and then remain in a relatively inert condition for a long time, until metamorphosis or later. Puckett (1940) showed that during this quiescent period of development it is impossible to affect the gonads by administration of sex hormones unless gonadotrophin is given at the same time. If gonadotrophin is given, the gonads are sensitized to sex hormones, and transformation of sex is obtained. SCHNEIDERMAN gave still another example from insects. The juvenile hormone has no action at all unless the prothoracic gland hormone, ecdysone, is present. The juvenile hormone modulates the effects of ecdysone on the cells of the insect. It apparently has no action of its own.

TONUTTI agreed with Segal that the full action with progesterone is obtained only when there is pretreatment with estradiol. But Hooker and Forbes (1947) found that there is a marked swelling of the nuclei of the uterine stroma without any preceding estradiol treatment. SEGAL then commented on the different situations encountered in these two cases. In the McPhail test, where estradiol is required first for a priming purpose, the condition of the entire uterus is evaluated, and the proliferation of the endometrium is examined histologically. In this case estradiol is almost certainly effective in causing a vascular proliferation prior to the progesterone effect; it thus appears that, for progesterone to have an effect on the entire gland, there must first be this preparation of the vascular bed and an increase in the vascularity of the uterus. TONUTTI pointed out that in the McPhail test the epithelium of the endometrium becomes higher and larger under the influence of estradiol. SEGAL agreed that this is so to a limited extent. Glandular proliferation is minimal with estradiol alone, if there is any at all. With the Hooker-Forbes test, where there is a direct action of progesterone alone, there is probably no real necessity for the vascular bed to be increased previously. Progesterone is administered locally, directly to the cells. The cells are exposed to the progesterone immediately without the necessity for an increased vascularity beforehand.

WEISS, again summarizing, indicated that each gland should be considered as composed of a glandular constituent, a stromal constituent, and a vascular constituent. In the past, little attention has been paid to the specific reactive capacities of the blood vessels and connective tissue; they were considered to be the same over the entire body. It now seems more likely that all three components of each gland are harmoniously differentiated in the same way. Thus all three components of an organ would seem to be specialized. The other possibility is, of course, that the primary action of a hormone is exerted on any one component, which then secondarily affects the other ones. This type of situation is encountered in the gonads, where the female component releases something that inhibits the male component. The decisive experiment would be to break up an organ into its three components by pure culture and then treat them alike. Will only one component respond, or will all three respond? The former should be the case if estrogen, for example, exerts a primary effect on one component of the uterus. But Weiss suspects that it will be possible in such an experiment to demonstrate an independent reaction of each component to the hormone. He asked whether tests of this sort had ever been made. He strongly suspects that the mosaic properties of the vascular tree and of the connective tissue will prove to be just as striking as the mosaic properties of the epithelial organs with which they are associated.

GAILLARD stated that he had not done quite the experiment suggested by Weiss, but a related one. If the ovaries of 3-week-old mice are cultured, the typical stroma changes during cultivation, and the typical interstitial cells disappear. If these cultures are then treated with gonadotrophins, there is no reaction whatsoever. But if the organ cultures are grafted back to a littermate, the typical interstitial elements reappear. Thus the stroma has retained its original specificity which it did not manifest under in vitro conditions; it then manifests its original specificity upon its return to the body. Except for these observations of Gaillard, no one seems to have made observations of the type suggested by Weiss. Both WILLIER and WEISS emphasized that this general problem has been neglected by endocrinologists as a group.

· IX ·

Ontogeny of Selected Hormone-dependent Receptors: Feather Papillae and Pigment Cells

The topic was introduced by DR. WILLIER, who recalled that many excellent studies have been made on the feather papilla and its contained melanoblasts as endocrine receptors. Male and female chickens of certain breeds can be distinguished from one another by the marked sexual dimorphism in the structure of their plumage. If a genetic female is castrated, the feather papilla produces, in certain regions of the body, a feather which is typically male in its structure. Since this is not true of all feather papillae, there apparently exists a differential sensitivity to the female sex hormone in the population of feather papillae. Each bird possesses approximately nine thousand such papillae, and each one gives its own distinctive and individual response to hormones. Feather papillae of castrated males likewise construct a male-type feather which differs from that of the normal male only in that it continues to grow almost indefinitely. If a feather is plucked in a castrated male, it begins to regenerate within 6 days. If it is plucked from a normal male, it will not regenerate until the next molting period. If the female hormone is added to either a castrated male or a castrated female, the feather papillae produce female-type feathers.

Plumage may show sexual dimorphism in pigmentation as well as in structure. One of the breeds in which melanoblasts are sensitive to sex hormone is the Brown Leghorn. In the male the breast feather is uniformly black, while in the female it is more or less salmon-colored. Complete castration of both male and female birds results in plumage that is male-type in both structure and pigmentation. The breast feathers are then uniformly black in both genetic males and genetic females in the total absence of sex hormones. Male hormones are unable to cause a change in the pigmentation of such castrates. Only an ovarian graft or an injection of estrogen can bring about a change in pigmentation from black to salmon, the female coloration. Under the influence of estrogen the melanoblasts of the growing breast feather differentiate into red melanophores rather than into black ones. Thus the melanoblasts of a

84

regenerating breast feather of either sex react to female, but not to male, hormone; they are sensitive to estrogens but are insensitive to androgens (Willier, 1950, 1953). The hormonal milieu can clearly change the direction of differentiation of the melanoblast in the Brown Leghorn.

Saddle feathers of castrates are long and acuminate. Their coloration is red primarily, indicating the action of pigment cells which produce red-pigment granules, although there is a small spot of black coloration, indicating, as well, the action of pigment cells containing black-pigment granules. Addition of estrogen causes the formation in regenerating feathers of a peculiar pattern which is a curious mixture of black- and red-pigment granules; the structure of the feather is also changed (see Willier, 1950, Fig. 2). Thyroxin also exerts an effect on plumage coloration in this breed; in general, it causes an extension of the amount of black pigment deposited within the feather during its development.

In a few instances races have originated in which the males exhibit hen-feathering almost identical with that of the females, i.e., there is little or no sexual dimorphism in plumage structure. In the complete absence of sex hormones in castrates of either sex, the feather papillae form cock feathers which are like those of normally cock-feathered breeds in shape and structure. In other words, the feather papillae of these breeds are conditioned to respond to either sex hormone equally well; they are insensitive to differences between them. The Silver Campine is an example of such a hen-feathered breed. There is little or no sexual dimorphism in feather structure or pigmentation. The adult plumage is barred black and white except for the hackle feathers, which are mostly white. In normal adult birds no red pigment is visible in the definitive feathers; yet a few red-pigment cells may be present in regenerating feathers. After castration of the male the plumage assumes the form of feathers characteristic of cocks of cock-feathered breeds, and red pigment appears in many regenerating feathers (Nickerson, 1946). Thus in the absence of male sex hormones, the formation of red pigment is no longer suppressed. The administration of either testosterone propionate or estradiol again suppresses the formation of red pigment, and in appropriate feathers the black-and-white barred pattern is restored (see Willier, 1950, Fig. 3). The melanoblast responds to each kind of sex hormone alike. It is therefore insensitive to differences between estradiol and testosterone.

Willier has summarized the evolution of the response of feather papillae and pigment cells to sex hormones (1950, Fig. 1). The starting point for this scheme is the Jungle Fowl, which exhibits sexual dimorphism in structure and color much like the Brown Leghorn. In such breeds the female hormone acts as the "sex differentiator" for the plumage. A mutation produced the breeds with hen-feathering, in which the feather papillae and pigment cells are sensitive to the presence of sex hormones but are unable to distinguish between male and female sex hormones. Other breeds have originated which have pigment cells that are insensitive to sex hormones. In such breeds the sex hormonal milieu can be changed repeatedly and even in a drastic manner, and still pigmentation is not affected. Still other breeds have evolved lethal-type pigment cells which are hormone-insensitive. Examples are the White Leghorns or White Wyandottes, which possess pigment cells, but these cells die prematurely before they have an opportunity to deposit pigment in regenerating feathers; consequently, the feathers remain white. But, if pigment cells from such breeds are cultivated in vitro, they form abundant pigment. WILLIER then presented his interpretative scheme of the interaction of feather papilla, melanoblast, and hormones encountered in the production of color patterns (Willier, 1952, Fig. 3).

The nature of the feather papilla was then examined in more detail. It is a complex morphologic unit which regularly regenerates a new feather after each molt or plucking throughout the life-span of the bird. It is composed of a specialized dermal papilla, which during regeneration becomes encircled by a thickened ring or "collar" of epidermal cells; the collar is invaded by melanoblasts. All the structural elements which make up the vane (rhachis and barbs) of the definitive feather originate as discrete, ridgelike outgrowths or sprouts from the apical margin of the epidermal collar. Melanoblasts enter these sprouts from the collar. Each sprout constantly increases in length by the addition of cells at its base from the collar; it also increases in length by elongation of the cells within the sprout. The number of melanoblasts fed into each forming sprout is exactly controlled in some way, as is their multiplication within the sprout. There is a certain population density of these pigment cells that is precisely controlled.

Intersecting the outgrowing barb ridges at a level just apical to the epidermal collar is a narrow transverse zone which is quite free of visible pigment cells. However, melanoblasts are present in this zone, as has been shown by appropriate tests of isolates for their capacity to form melanophores. At the apical border of the pigment-free zone the melanoblasts first begin the synthesis of visible melanin pigment granules and soon assume the characteristics of typical branched melanophores. It is here that the direction of differentiation of hormone-sensitive melanoblasts is first influenced by sex hormones. For example, when female sex hormones are added to Brown Leghorn castrates, the melanoblasts in this region no longer differentiate into black melanophores but now differentiate into melanophores containing red pigment. As long as female sex hormone is present in adequate amounts, red pigment will be produced and deposited at the base of an otherwise black feather. If female hormone is not added, black melanophores then appear in this zone of differentiation. Thus the period during which female hormone was present during the development of a feather is recorded permanently as a red band across the feather. Thus it is possible, by injecting female hormone and then by discontinuing injections and then by injecting them again, etc., to produce a feather with alternate black and red transverse bands. Such patterns were first produced by Dr. Mary Juhn. She did not go to the laboratory on Sunday, and her failure to inject female sex hormone on that day was recorded permanently as a black bar on a red feather; such bars could appropriately be called "Sabbath bars."

Other complex experiments have been performed on feather papillae by Wang (1943, 1948). He removed dermal papillae from feather follicles in the saddle region and then transplanted them to feather follicles in the breast region which were deprived of their dermal papillae. The epidermis of the empty breast follicles covers the transplanted dermal papillae originating from saddle follicles, and the composite feather papillae then form feathers whose form is characteristic of that of the *breast* feather tract. The transplanted dermal papilla from the saddle region exerts an inductor-like action on the epidermis of the breast follicle, but the response that is obtained is the only one that the breast epidermis is capable of giving, namely, formation of a typical breast-type feather. If female sex hormone is given to the castrated bird possessing such a composite feather papilla and treatment is then discontinued, a transverse red bar can be recorded on this feather just as if it were developing from a normal breast feather papilla.

Thus the feather papilla is a remarkable example of an endocrine end organ which can be rather thoroughly analyzed with respect to its powers of response to changes in the hormonal milieu. And, as stated before, there are about nine thousand different feather papillae on one bird, each responding in a different way to changes in the hormonal milieu. Different papillae, even within a single feather tract, give different responses. Thus the response of endocrine receptors can vary with their positions on the body.

BURNS then raised two questions. He inquired, first, whether the lethal action encountered in pigment cells of White Leghorns and White Wyandottes, which destroys them before they have an opportunity to deposit pigment, is due to a mutation acting within the pigment cell or whether it acts primarily in the surrounding tissue, thereby killing the pigment cell indirectly. WILLIER answered that there is no question about this; it is acting within the pigment cell itself. If White Leghorn pigment cells are transplanted to a black breed, they cause formation of white feathers on that breed. When they get into a feather papilla that normally would contain pigment, they still behave just as they would in a papilla of a White Leghorn. They die precociously. They form some pigment, and they also form pigment in vitro, as has already been mentioned. But they suddenly pull in their processes and die. Occasionally they even deposit a few pigment granules before they die, but only rarely. Their life-span in tissue culture is about 3 days, contrasted with the life-span of pigment cells of Barred Plymouth Rocks, which survive up to 10 days after explantation. This has been worked out carefully by Hamilton (1940). The gene for white in White Leghorns is a dominant gene. Other white breeds, such as White Plymouth Rocks, have a recessive gene for white; their pigment cells die even more precociously in vitro than those of dominant white breeds. Thus it appears that there is no question that the lethal factor is operating within the pigment cell itself. There is also another line of evidence in favor of this conclusion. When pigment cells are transplanted from any colored breed to White Leghorn hosts, these pigment cells survive in feather papillae of the latter and produce and deposit their pigment, thus forming in host feathers a color pattern typical of the donor.

The second comment made by BURNS was more in the nature of a remark than a question. He emphasized that the feather papilla is a receptor which, in a particular part of the body, produces a feather of a particular morphology and particular shape which can be changed by the action of hormones. And this papilla contains pigment cells which produce a pigment the color of which changes with certain types of hormones. In all these experiments the changes have, presumably, been induced by injection of pure steroid hormones. Have all these changes been induced systematically by transplantation of gonad tissue, and, if so, do the results correspond *exactly* with those produced by pure steroid hormones? He emphasized that this is an important question relative to the problem as to how closely pure hormones represent or approximate the natural hormone. Apparently, the feather germ provides a system in which this problem can be checked rather minutely to determine whether pure hormones do produce exactly the same changes with respect to the form of the feather, with respect to the color of the pigment, with respect to the band pattern, etc., as do grafts of the natural gland. WILLIER answered that female sex hormones do produce exactly the same effects as an ovarian graft, for example. BURNS then concluded that it is impossible in a rather complex system involving two or three factors like form, color, and band pattern to distinguish between the two substances, that produced by the gland and that produced by the synthetic hormone, the presumption being, therefore, that they must be very similar or identical compounds. WEISS, however, pointed out that even from such an analysis it is not possible to decide whether the two substances are identical or whether the receptor system is not sufficiently discriminative for it to make any difference. After all, as Willier stated earlier, pigment cells in some breeds respond indiscriminately even to male and female hormones.

WEISS inquired whether any experiments have been done with local implantation of pellets and, if so, whether this changes the feathers locally. WILLIER answered that such experiments have been done by Greenwood and Blyth (1935), although they were done by local injection of female sex hormone at a dosage which was not effective in the systematic circulation but was effective only locally in the injected feather tract. The feathers in the process of regeneration close to the injection site form red coloration; those at some distance from the injection site show no reaction. There is a diffusion of the hormone from the site of injection. Some feathers are obtained which show a reaction to the hormone on one side and no reaction on the opposite side; so there can be different reactions under these circumstances on the two sides of the same shaft.

SEGAL then discussed hormonal control of pigmentation in various African weaver finches. This work has recently been reviewed by Witschi (1955) in a paper which contains a colored illustration to demonstrate the feather and bill reactions discussed below. Feather coloration of the Napolean weaver finch (*Pyromelana*) exhibits a seasonal dimorphism. The breast feathers of either a male or a female bird are non-colored during the quiescent season. Non-breeding birds, either male or female, also have ivory-colored bills. As the breeding season approaches, both sexes molt and assume a new plumage for the breeding season. The female shows no difference in feather coloration from before the molt. The male assumes a gaudy yellow-and-black garb. The breast feathers, which are the only ones to be discussed here, are black. The bill of the male gradually blackens as the breeding season approaches.

Contrary to expectation, the yearly appearance of the nuptial plumage of the male is not controlled by androgens from the testis. Removal of the testes does not terminate this seasonal variation in the male plumage. However, following castration of the male, the bill color no longer turns black with approach of the breeding season but remains ivory-colored all year round. Hence a castrate during the breeding season has a bright-colored nuptial plumage but the quiescent, ivory-colored bill. This indicates that melanin deposition in the bill is controlled by gonadal hormones. Injection of androgen into a castrate male or female results in blackening of the bill. Injection of androgen into a female or a male out of breeding season (castrate or intact) fails to bring on melanin deposition in regenerating feathers. After several attempts to induce nuptial plumage development with androgens and other steroid hormones had failed, it was observed that this result could be achieved by the administration of pituitary extract. It should be emphasized that none of the non-hypophyseal hormones—and all were tested—would give the response. This aggregate of results indicates that a hypophyseal factor has a *direct* action in causing melanin deposition by the melanocytes of the breast feathers. By the method of elimination to find the active principle, it was discovered to be the luteinizing hormone (LH) of the anterior pituitary. It has since been found that human chorionic gonadotrophin and pregnant mare serum, both containing the luteinizing principle, also cause feather blackening in these birds. This effect is directly on the melanocytes of feather tracts and is not mediated through the gonads, since a positive response is obtained in castrate birds.

In a closely related bird, the Paradise Wydah, LH causes the deposition of melanin not only in the feathers but also in the bill. Castration of the Paradise Wydah causes no change whatsoever in the seasonal dimorphism. Both feather and bill blackening continue to occur annually in castrate males. Injection of LH can induce the appearance of both nuptial characteristics—black bill and black breast feathers—in a female or in a male during the quiescent season.

Two points deserve particular emphasis. First, in the same bird, the Napoleon weaver finch, the same cell type in different locations responds to different hormones. The melanocytes of the bill are unaffected by LH directly but are stimulated to deposit melanin by androgen. The melanocytes of the feathers are unaffected by androgens but are stimulated to deposit melanin by LH directly. Second, between the two types of birds, the same morphologic structure—the bill—has changed its responsiveness from one hormone to another. In the case of the Napoleon weaver finch it responds to androgen; in the Paradise Wydah it responds to LH.

WEISS inquired whether adrenalin is effective. SEGAL answered that adrenalectomy of these birds has never been performed but that attempts have been made to elicit this coloration response with corticoids or with adrenocorticotrophic hormones, without success. TONUTTI expressed his surprise that a tissue can react to LH without intervention of the gonads. He inquired about the kind of LH that was used. SEGAL answered that this is one of the few examples of the response of a peripheral tissue to a trophic hormone, peripheral, that is, outside the gonads. The LH that was used came from various sources. The so-called purified LH fraction was obtained from all the suppliers in this country, like Armour. Li in California provided some, as did McShan at Wisconsin and others who have been attempting to purify LH as such.

SCHNEIDERMAN pointed out that this is one of the most striking examples of the ability of an end organ to capture hormones. Certainly these two end organs seem to capture different hormones and to have changed the hormones that they were originally responsive to. SEGAL agreed that this does appear to represent an evolutionary shift from the direct use of gonadotrophic hormone to perhaps a later stage of evolutionary history in which the intermediary action of the gonads comes into play.

WEISS then inquired whether it is possible that some other organ is providing the hormone in certain cases of so-called hormone-insensitive pigment cells which show no change in behavior in the absence of a particular gonad. Perhaps two glands share the same function, and, if so, the removal of both glands would be necessary to demonstrate that the pigment cells are actually hormone-sensitive. Perhaps the action of thyroxin in extending pigmentation of the feathers is a tendency in that direction. MÜHLBOCK inquired whether Willier had done any experiments involving antagonism between the male and female hormone. He mentioned that he had carried out such an experiment some years ago (Mühlbock, 1939) but that no antagonism was indicated. In his experiments, testosterone did not counteract the effects of estrogenic hormone. He suggested that someone with Willier's experience might learn more about the mechanisms involved with the use of such an approach.

· X ·

Synergistic Action of Hormones

WEISS stated that two agents are said to be "synergistic" whose effects are additive along any particular linear scale involving, for example, size of the nucleus or cell, thickness of an epithelium, number of cells, etc. If two agents produce subtractive effects along the linear scale, they would be exerting inhibitory or antagonistic actions. It is not possible to analyze the real operation of a synergistic system but only the external criteria, which provide the only way of measuring the system, and they are limited. BURNS mentioned the possibility of confusing what has already been discussed as a conditioning effect of one hormone followed by the action of another with true synergism, which implies two hormones acting together simultaneously. When two hormones are administered separately in time, one definitely in advance of the other, a true conditioning effect might be suspected, but it is also possible that when two hormones are given simultaneously, one hormone is conditioning while the other is exploiting what has been conditioned. WEISS agreed that the fact that two hormones are administered simultaneously does not guarantee that the cell will be exposed to both of them at the same time or in the same way. It is true that all too often the time of administration is confused with the time of action, about which literally nothing is known. There is always a lag period, which varies, depending on permeability and accessibility, and this ought to be emphasized.

WILLIER recalled again, as he had done earlier in the introduction to the conference, that Smith (1933) was the first to emphasize that a synergism occurs between thyroxin and a growth-promoting factor from the anterior pituitary. He showed that an anterior pituitary extract, not a purified hormone, has a growth-promoting effect on hypophysectomized rats and that administration of thyroxin simultaneously causes an augmentation of growth beyond that produced by the pituitary extract alone. Subsequently, Evans and Simpson and others have shown with purified hormones that the so-called growth hormone has a promoting effect on growth which becomes even greater when thyroxin is given simultaneously.

92

The work of one of his collaborators, Dr. de Voogd v/d Straaten (unpublished) was then discussed by GAILLARD. He has been studying the effect of estrogen and of progesterone either separately or in combination on the process of fibrocytosis in human neutrophilic granulocytes. The particles to be phagocytosed are composed of shellac, Janus green, and normal actylic alcohol and are attached to the fibrin fibers of the clot on which the granulocytes are distributed at random. The granulocytes move along the fibers and phagocytose the particles. In the presence of 0.075 μg. of estrone, about 70 per cent of the granulocytes derived from a male appear to have ingested one or more particles. Progesterone (0.05 μg.) leads to roughly 65 per cent of the cells with phagocytosed particles. Addition of 0.075 μg. of estrone plus 0.05 μg. of progesterone to the same preparation leads to about 90 per cent of the cells showing phagocytic activity. In control preparations without any hormone added to the medium, about 59 per cent of the granulocytes show phagocytosis. The high percentage of cells exhibiting phagocytosis after the simultaneous addition of the two hormones suggests a synergistic effect. WEISS pointed out that the effect of the two acting simultaneously is actually more than the sum of the effects of the two hormones separately. Thus the two hormones mutually reinforce each other in some way. But, since they work in the same direction, this certainly is a case of synergism. GAILLARD then emphasized that the above results are obtained only with exactly calibrated dosages. No effect at all occurs with the wrong doses.

Reactions of leukocytes from females are different and are related to the menstrual cycle. Granulocytes taken from the pre-ovulatory period do not react after the addition of estrogen. Phagocytosis increases significantly, however, if a combination of progesterone and estrogen is given. Granulocytes taken immediately after ovulation behave quite differently. The addition of 0.1 μg. of estrogen gives a significant rise in the percentage of cells showing phagocytosis, while the combination of progesterone and estrogen produces a decrease in the number of cells containing phagocytosed particles. From the twenty-fourth day of the cycle on, this effect becomes less pronounced, and, by the time of the menstrual bleeding, the effect characteristic of the pre-ovulatory period reappears. It seems that the observed differences in behavior depend on the amount of estrogen and/or progesterone present in the female blood.

SCHNEIDERMAN asked whether the blood cells were washed and put in the serum. GAILLARD said this was not done. They used 0.05 cc. of capillary blood, to which was added 0.02 cc. of the reagent containing the gum acacia, boric acid, and particles to be phagocytosed, as well as the hormones to be tested. The mixture is introduced into a capillary chamber and is centrifuged slightly during $\frac{3}{4}$ minute before coagulation occurs. In this way a red and a white clot are obtained. The cells in the white clot are used for the observations after an incubation period of $2\frac{1}{2}$ hours at $37°$ C. Dr. de Voogd v/d Straaten has studied seven complete cycles, and, with the exception of one case, the effects were as described above.

WEISS pointed out that there appears to be an actual sex difference in the leukocytes. GAILLARD answered that the activity of the leukocytes of the female is different from that of the male when they are in female serum. But if the male leukocytes are given the same combination of estrone and progesterone, they behave just as if they are female. WEISS then asked whether this means that there is no basic sex difference in the leukocytes of males and females. Is their behavior due entirely to the serum containing them? GAILLARD stated that he did not believe this to be true. SCHNEIDERMAN then inquired what happens if the cells are washed. GAILLARD answered that washing probably induces considerable change in the surface of the cells, although they have never actually studied this. WEISS pointed out that this is another striking example of the effects of sex hormones on the properties of a cellular population that would not normally be suspected.

TONUTTI then discussed an observation of Hisaw *et al.* (1954), which is pertinent to the topic. Two estrogens—namely, estradiol and its metabolite, estrone—both have a growth-promoting action on the uterus. But if these two estrogens are given together, their effects are not additive. Estrone seems to have an inhibiting action on the effect of estradiol. This shows how complicated the interaction of two hormones can be, even when they have the same specific effect. WEISS asked whether this is necessarily conclusive. If a detector is used which has a ceiling on its production, can you step up that production above its ceiling? Obviously, once a reacting tissue has reached its maximum capacity, it cannot be driven any higher. He wanted to be certain that this possibility is excluded. TONUTTI answered that they use a very low dosage of estradiol. If a higher dosage is used, it is very easy to increase the weight of the uterus five to ten times. This, then, avoids the possible criticism suggested by Weiss.

SEGAL mentioned that they (Wicks and Segal, 1956) have just finished repeating this work in mice and that some additional comments are pertinent. The inhibiting interaction of the two estrogens can be summarized as follows: The uterine response to estradiol in immature female mice is inhibited significantly by concurrent injection of estriol.

The extent of inhibition is proportionate to the amount of estriol added. The impeding interaction occurs along the ascending segment of the estradiol dose-response curve, and with higher doses as well. In no case does a combination of these estrogens have a positive additive effect. These conclusions are based on both wet and dry uterine weight determinations. Day-by-day analysis shows that uterine weight gain during each 24-hour period of estradiol treatment is inhibited when estriol is given concurrently. The total results negate the possibilities that the estriol-estradiol interaction is a masked summation effect in which time of maximum effect has shifted, or that an additive effect occurs in which the two estrogens combined exceed the maximum response dose. Rather it appears that estriol competes actively at a physiologic site essential in the development of the usual estradiol stimulation of the uterus. WEISS inquired whether this could be tested by changing the timing of administration of the two with respect to each other. SEGAL stated that this is to be the next step in the program. WEISS asked whether these two molecules are closely related in structure. SEGAL replied that they are very similar. WEISS then suggested that the results might be explainable by the population density of the two types or that there might be an actual steric interference at the same site, just as in the case of structural analogs. But he also pointed out that the discussion is now centered around inadequate replicas of some natural agents and that their effect might not apply in the natural situation.

SEGAL then commented on the way Szego and Roberts (1948) would interpret an experiment of this sort. They believe that, before estradiol can exert an effect on a target organ, it must first be conjugated with a protein probably at the liver site. Estriol is the more polar of these two compounds, and, by virtue of this character, it would have a tendency to enter into a protein complex more selectively. Thus perhaps the sites for activation of the estrogen are being selectively occupied by the estriol by virtue of its greater polarity.

MOOG then commented on the work of Bullough (1950) on mitosis in vitro. He took small pieces of ear epidermis and studied its rate of mitosis in tissue culture. The rate of mitosis is always rather uniform in epidermis taken from males, provided that the tissue is taken at the same time each day. By contrast, the rate of mitosis differs considerably in epidermis taken from females, depending on the time of the cycle when the epidermis is taken. If it is isolated at a time when a high titer of estrogen is expected in the blood stream of the female, the isolated material continues to show the influence of estrogen for a number of hours. Apparently, the epidermal material carries along a supply of the hormone which lasts for some time. But if the epidermis is kept in isolation for several hours, the estrogen effect disappears. The mitotic rate then drops.

WEISS then inquired whether there is any synergistic effect that works on mitosis by way of the pancreas. There are two agents which can produce mitotic stimulation locally when grafted under starved amphibian skin. One is the central nervous system, which has a special carbohydrate requirement; the other is the pancreas. They seem to have nothing in common except that carbohydrate metabolism is important to both. He also inquired about the possibility of an inner antagonism between insulin and glucagon, the products of beta and alpha cells, respectively. TONUTTI stated that it is well known that steroid diabetes can be induced in the guinea pig with high doses of cortisone (Hausberger and Ramsay, 1953, 1955). Fabbrini (1955*b*, 1956) studied in his laboratory the influence of cortisone on the nuclear size of the alpha and beta cells in the guinea pig. Only the beta cells show an increased nuclear volume. The alpha cells remain unchanged. The ratio of alpha to beta cells (normally about 20/80) remains unchanged. Since the islets become very large, there must be an increase in both beta and alpha cells. Mitosis of beta cells also occurs. When the animals are treated simultaneously with cortisone and insulin, the beta cells remain unchanged; their nuclear volume and the number of mitoses do not increase under these circumstances.

WEISS then asked whether cortisone alone causes a mitotic response of the skin. He inquired about the response to cortisone in wound healing. TONUTTI stated that it is diminished in the rat but not in the guinea pig. WEISS then inquired whether the reduction in wound healing is in terms of mitotic activity or of migration of cells. GAILLARD answered that it is the migration of cells which is affected. SCHOTTÉ recalled that Manner (1955) had recently demonstrated a decrease in mitotic activity in the skin of the newt after application of cortisone.

Attention was then called by WILLIER to the studies of his student, Konigsberg (1954), and others on the level of blood glucose in the chick embryo. The concentration of blood glucose is expressed as milligrams per cent. Presumably, glucose is present in the blood from the onset of circulation. It enters the blood from the yolk sac, which, according to Claude Bernard, functions as a liver. The blood-sugar level rises until the tenth day of incubation, remains relatively constant until the fourteenth day, and then increases considerably by the sixteenth day (see Konigsberg, 1954, Fig. 1). What regulates these changing levels of blood glucose? What causes these shifts in steady state with time? By 10 days the thyroid follicles are beginning to accumulate thyroglobulin. Even earlier, adrenalin or noradrenalin is present in the embryonic adrenals. Ascorbic acid and lipids are accumulating in the adrenal cortex during this period, and these products are indicators of the functional activity of the cortex. The beta cells appear in the pancreas by the twelfth or thirteenth day. All these endocrine glands are producing hormones which are involved in sugar metabolism in posthatching stages, at which times their actions are interlocked in complex ways. Whether the hormones produced by these embryonic glands are actually released into the circulation is uncertain, but, in mammals, capillaries become associated with the beta cells of the pancreas at about the time that the secretion granules appear in these cells, providing the necessary structural relationship for release of insulin into the blood. The anterior pituitary gland is certainly involved in some way, directly or indirectly, because there is a marked elevation in the blood-sugar level following hypophysectomy (Konigsberg, 1954, Fig. 1). Much remains to be learned about the development of homeostasis or steady states in the embryo, and the factors which control the blood-sugar level are especially intriguing because of the shifts in steady state of this level with time.

SCHNEIDERMAN asked whether it is possible that the regulation of the level of blood sugar is simply the consequence of changes in the kinds of tissues that are present at different stages. Perhaps there is no real hormonal regulation at all in these early stages but simply a series of changes in the distribution of glucose between the new tissues. MOOG stated that this is not very likely because, in the very period when the leveling-off of blood sugar occurs, there is a loss of glycogen from the liver. It would seem that the blood-sugar level should increase under those circumstances. WILLIER asked Moog if she has confirmed the plateau period in any of her work. She replied that she has not done any blood-sugar work but that she has worked with liver glycogen and does find a definite drop in the latter at the time that the level of the blood sugar remains constant. BURNS mentioned that Jost (1953) reported a big drop in liver glycogen in the rabbit fetus after the pituitary is removed by decapitation. Seven to 8 days after decapitation, the liver glycogen dropped to about 15 per cent of its original value.

WEISS stated that he felt these remarks to be particularly significant when the work of Landauer and Zwilling is recalled (Landauer, 1945, 1947a, b; Landauer and Bliss, 1946; Landauer and Lang, 1946; Zwilling, 1948). They demonstrated the significance of maintaining an appropriate steady state because the slightest deviation from this state has

97

very serious morphogenetic effects on development. If insulin is injected around 4 days, hypoglycemia results, and the embryos that develop are rumpless, sirenoids, or exhibit various other kinds of malformations of the skeletal system. Apparently the level of blood glucose at each stage of normal development is harmonized with the requirements of that particular stage. When the level falls below the requirements, developmental abnormalities are the consequence. Weiss inquired what happens if insulin is injected as late as 12 days of incubation. He wondered whether it has an effect after the homeostatic mechanism is established. The question remained unanswered. Weiss also inquired whether there is an effect of the insulin on the pancreas when it is injected later. Does it cause a compensatory retrenchment of pancreatic differentiation? Again there was no information.

WILLIER pursued the matter of the complexity of the endocrine control of sugar metabolism even further, pointing out that it is necessary, when development of these systems is studied, to keep in mind what is known about the adult. The adrenals produce adrenalin, which exerts a hyperglycemic effect. It can act directly on the liver. It can also act through the hypothalamus, then through the posterior pituitary via neurosecretory nerves, then through the portal circulation between the posterior pituitary and anterior pituitary, and the anterior pituitary can send a message to the alpha cells. Embryologists must explain how these things become established during the formation of the embryo and determine the time at which they come into play. When are these mechanisms established? Are they established in a certain sequence? MOOG inquired whether the thyroid should not be invoked also, in view of the work of Konigsberg (1954). WILLIER agreed that the thyroid certainly plays a role. Moreover, there is evidence that the so-called purified growth hormone has a hyperglycemic effect, the idea being that it acts on the alpha cells. This has been worked out by Young (1953) in England.

TONUTTI mentioned that in his laboratory the influence of the so-called growth hormone on the ratio of alpha to beta cells in young rats was studied by Thiermer (1953) and that this ratio remained unchanged. The rats respond well with accelerated growth following administration of growth hormone preparations, but there is no detectable influence on the alpha cells. This study does not substantiate Young's claims. At least in the morphologic sense, no action of the growth hormone on alpha cells is demonstrated. This was an Armour growth hormone that was used. WILLIER then asked whether Tonutti would agree that the growth hormone has a hyperglycemic effect. TONUTTI agreed that it has a diabetogenic action, but he emphasized that this does not necessarily mean that the diabetogenic action is exerted through the alpha cells.

MÜHLBOCK then turned the discussion to some of their work at the Amsterdam Cancer Institute, where the center of interest is the relationship between hormones and the genesis of cancer, especially in mice. The main object of study is the genesis of mammary cancer; consequently, interest centers mostly on the function of the hypophysis and ovaries. It is well known that the hormonal function of the ovaries can be followed readily by taking vaginal smears. The ovarian function in various strains of mice has been followed throughout life by means of vaginal-smear studies, and a curious phenomenon was observed. The normal estrous cycle lasts for 4–6 days, and cycles normally follow one another quite regularly. Frequently, however, this regular periodicity is interrupted by prolonged 8-day diestrous intervals. Van der Lee and Boot (1955, 1956) investigated the meaning of these diestrous periods. They demonstrated that these periods represent spontaneous pseudo-pregnancies. This means that all hormonal changes occur as in a normal pregnancy except that there are no fertilized ova and hence the placenta is absent. This period of pseudo-pregnancy lasts only half the time of a normal pregnancy, that is, 10–12 days. When fertilized ova are transferred from another animal into the uterus of a pseudo-pregnant mouse, the ova undergo implantation, and the pseudo-pregnancy is converted into a true pregnancy in which the young are born at term (Boot and Mühlbock, 1953).

Such spontaneous pseudo-pregnancies are observed regularly only when at least two female mice are kept together in a cage. Female mice kept in isolation show the phenomenon much less frequently. When a number of mice that had been kept separately for a period of time are subsequently put together, four to a cage, nearly all the mice become pseudo-pregnant at once. It is, of course, known that pseudo-pregnancy can be induced by mating with a sterilized male mouse. Consequently, it was suspected that perhaps these spontaneous pseudo-pregnancies were induced by close bodily contact among the females. But it was then found that if the mice are kept four to a cage, but separated from each other by a partition of wire mesh, spontaneous pseudo-pregnancies continue to occur. The role of sight and smell in this phenomenon was then tested. Ablation of the olfactory lobes in the $C_{57}B1$ strain is followed by nearly total disappearance of spontaneous pseudo-pregnancies; the sequence of the cycles then becomes quite regular (Fig. 10). Thus an olfactory stimulus appears to be responsible for the induction of these pseudo-pregnancies. This means that an olfactory stimulus can lead to the release of prolactin from the anterior lobe of the pituitary. WEISS asked whether the results are any different if females are exposed to males rather than to other females. MÜHLBOCK replied that this experiment has not been done.

WILLIER remarked that such experiments reminded him of the results obtained by Olsen and Marsden (1954), of the Agricultural Experiment Station at Beltsville, Maryland. Turkeys occasionally lay parthenogenetic eggs. They observed that a greater percentage of parthenogenetic eggs is obtained from those females that can see a gobbler in the distance.

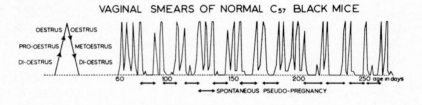

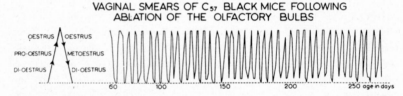

FIG. 10.—Effect of ablation of the olfactory bulbs upon the occurrence of spontaneous pseudo-pregnancies. (Mühlbock, original.)

WEISS then discussed some experiments carried out with Dr. Jane Overton (Weiss and Overton, 1954; Overton, 1955). If amphibian urodele larvae are starved, the mitotic activity in the skin is reduced from sixty dividing cells per thousand cells examined to practically zero. The drop in mitosis is rather sudden. If a graft of nerve tissue is placed under the skin, mitotic activity flares up locally in the starved animal and then fades out again. If the animal is first starved and then is well fed, mitotic activity goes up and comes down to about 50 per cent of its maximum, even when feeding continues. This response occurs over the entire skin, so there is enormous mitotic activity at this time. WEISS suspected that part of this stimulation might be the result of the presence of food, the rest due to actual consumption of food. Observations by Overton (unpublished) seem to indicate that this might be the case. If the animals are kept completely starved and are then shown food but are not permitted to eat it, they show a mitotic wave in the skin. WEISS suggested that this works from the visual centers through the hypothalamus to the pituitary and from there, perhaps, through the pancreas. Apparently, there are quite a number of similar situations in which the nervous system acts through the hormonal system to affect growth. KOLLROS inquired whether the sense of smell might be involved rather than vision. WEISS answered that he did not know the experiments in detail.

A remark by Professor Pumphrey (1955) was then read by WILLIER. Pumphrey is a neurologist, but he was invited to make the introductory remarks at the conference on comparative endocrinology of vertebrates held at the University of Liverpool in 1954. "It was almost exactly twenty years ago that C. N. Long, then in Philadelphia, coined the epigram: 'the pituitary is the conductor of the glandular orchestra.' This observation is still quoted and still seems apt, but it has, I think, acquired a *new look*. Today, if I have the picture correctly, the pituitary conducts by permission, and each member of the orchestra has a clause in his contract entitling him to switch the conductor off when he has had enough. The concept of feedback which has overrun neurology is obviously casting its long shadow over endocrinology." WILLIER then added, paraphrasing Pumphrey to some extent, that it seems surprising that questions of feedback were not raised twenty years ago. The fact that these questions are being asked today is a measure of the change in emphasis which has taken place in twenty years. This feedback mechanism is a most extraordinary one and has been neglected. The pituitary stimulates an endocrine receptor; the endocrine receptor produces hormones which are poured into the circulation. When a certain quantitative level is reached, they somehow or other tell the pituitary to stop.

WEISS then commented that feedback mechanisms also act between homologous organs and that this problem has been analyzed mathematically (Weiss and Kavanau, 1957). Briefly, each organ or each cell type produces inhibitors of its own growth, and the total concentration of these in the circulation comes into equilibrium with the productive or generative mass to produce a steady state. Any interference with the products in circulation will automatically shift the equilibrium away from the intracellular concentration of inhibitors in the direction of the pool, so that part of the cellular content will be "disinhibited," so to speak, automatically. This works for liver cells and kidney cells and for several specific glandular types. Dr. Teir (Teir *et al.*, 1957) is working this out for the supraorbital glands. It also works for the different types

101

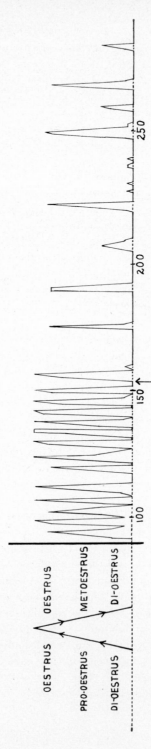

FIG. 11.—Estrus cycle in mice before and after subcutaneous implantation of 5 hypophyses of the same strain. ↑ = time of implantation. Age is indicated in days. Redrawn from Mühlbock and Boot (1957).

of blood cells during blood regeneration. It is quite possible that a similar mechanism operates between any pair of endocrine organs so that what one releases acts as an inhibitor of the other. Instead of the cell releasing autoinhibitors, it acts on the paired or matched organ, the product of which will serve as an inhibitor for that particular organ. Thus the pituitary, for example, would inhibit itself through the thyroid, instead of through its own agency. Perhaps the hormonal mechanisms of inhibition can be visualized as the evolution of specialization of the more general feedback system.

KOLLROS then called attention to an experiment of Blount (1935), in which a salamander larva is made hyperpituitary by grafting to it two extra pituitaries at the rudiment stage. Growth and metamorphosis are then studied. Metamorphosis does not occur early but takes place at the same time in normal controls and in the triple-pituitary animals. Thus some regulation occurs to control the production of TSH at normal levels, but apparently the production of growth hormone is not controlled, since the body proportions of operated animals are substantially changed, although the over-all size of the triple-pituitary animals is substantially less than that of controls.

MÜHLBOCK stated that he has done experiments in which extra pituitaries are transplanted subcutaneously in mice (Mühlbock and Boot, 1956). By examination of the estrous cycle in the operated animals it can be demonstrated that frequent pseudo-pregnancies occur (Fig. 11). It follows that the hypophysis, when transplanted subcutaneously, produces prolactin independently of the hypothalamus.

· XI ·

Integration of the Endocrine System

Emphasis was placed by DR. WEISS on the development of the endocrine *system*. How does harmony develop between the endocrines and their receptor organs? And by "receptor organs" is also meant other endocrines which are at one time an emitter and at another time a receptor. Actually, it is doubtful whether there is any functional cell in the body which does not produce some effects on other cells via the circulation. The only difference between the endocrine system proper and the production of other types of cell-specific secretions that may affect other types of cells may be the fact that the endocrine system works with predestined types of receivers. Thus in the endocrine system there are pairs of matched organs: an emitter with an attuned receptor. Non-endocrine systems may work in a more general way. But on the molecular level it may be that something produced by the skin may have a very specific molecular receptor elsewhere. Even within the endocrine system the statement that matching pairs of organs are involved is an oversimplification which has only been introduced into the literature because some of the paired responses are the most conspicuous ones. Practically every one of the endocrine glands has some less conspicuous effects which are of a more universal nature, affecting metabolic processes all over the body. There is a vast humoral communication system in which each tissue can communicate with all the other tissues by mechanisms with different degrees of chemical specificity. "Chemical specificity" means that there is a coded message that operates by virtue of something like the steric conformity of a molecule, like the way a coded message works when punched on an IBM card. That code has all degrees of detail or specificity, but it is a very universal language which affects all cells to a certain extent, as in the case of those that affect metabolism in general or calcium metabolism or sugar metabolism. More organs in the future may have to be included as part of the endocrine system.

TONUTTI then discussed the whole interacting endocrine system as a unit rather than the individual pieces of the system. He pointed out how difficult a task it is to outline in a schematic manner the interrelations

104

among the different endocrine glands. It is possible to give a picture of the basic actions and interactions of hormones only in an oversimplified manner (Fig. 12).

It is well established today that the hypothalamus exerts control over many functions of the hypophysis, such as production and release of ACTH, TSH, FSH, and LH (see Harris, 1955; Fields, Guillemin, and Carton, 1956). As was pointed out by Dr. Mühlbock earlier, the production of luteotrophin (LTH) is independent of hypothalamic control, since this hormone is also produced by pituitary grafts placed under the skin in heterotopic positions. STH or the so-called growth hormone seems to have some indirect control over the islands of Langerhans and the parathyroids, but there are some intermediate mechanisms which are not understood at the present time. The indirect influence of STH on the islands of Langerhans is mediated by the blood glucose (A), and the influence on the parathyroids by the level of blood phosphorus (B) (see Törnblom, 1949; Engfeldt, 1950). Thyrotrophic hormone (TSH) influences the structure of the thyroid and stimulates production and release of thyroxin and triiodothyronine (C). Both products of the thyroid diminish the production and release of thyrotrophin from the anterior pituitary by a feedback mechanism (D). Both hormones can also diminish the growth-promoting action of a given amount of TSH on thyroid cells (E). This interference of thyroid hormones with the action of thyrotrophin on thyroid cells can be demonstrated in the hypopysectomized rat. The growth-promoting effect of a given amount of TSH (as revealed by measurement of the height of thyroid cells) is diminished if the animals are treated simultaneously with thyroxin (Rawson and Money, 1949) or with triiodothyronine (Fabbrini, 1955a).

ACTH influences the structure of the adrenal cortex and stimulates the production and release of cortical hormones (F). Only glucocorticoids have a pronounced influence on the production and release of ACTH from the pituitary (G). FSH acts on testis tubules and stimulates spermatogenesis (H). LH (or ICSH) promotes the differentiation of the Leydig cells of the testis (I) or ovaries (J) and stimulates these cells to produce androgens and estrogens. Both androgens (K) and estrogens (L) are able to inhibit the gonadotrophic activity of the anterior pituitary. The structure and function of testis tubules are also under the influence of androgens produced by the Leydig cells under the control of ICSH (M). It is well known that tubular damage without disturbance of testicular androgen production may stimulate the production and release of gonadotrophins. McCullagh *et al.* (1950) believe, therefore, that the tubules produce a second testicular hormone, called

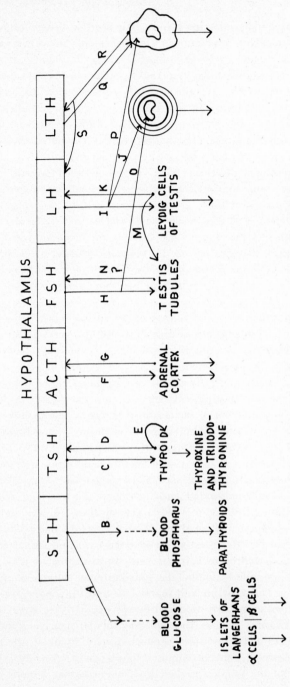

Fig. 12.—Interactions within the endocrine system. (Tonutti, original.)

"inhibine," which counteracts especially the FSH activity of the pituitary (*N*). The existence of this hormone is doubted by other authors, who suspect that it is simply estrogen produced by the tubules or by the Leydig cells.

FSH is responsible for the growth of secondary follicles and the formation of mature follicles (*O*). But even in the complete absence of the pituitary, secondary follicles of small size are still growing. The production of small follicles is therefore an autonomous process, and only the formation of medium-sized and mature follicles is dependent upon the presence of FSH. Theca interna tissue is produced simultaneously with the growth of follicles, but there is no production of estrogen unless stimulated by LH (*J*). In the absence of this hormone as a consequence of hypophysectomy, the cells of the theca interna and all cells which are derived from the theca interna (interstitial cells of the ovary or "theca-organs") undergo atrophy. On the other hand, administration of LH to hypophysectomized animals leads to pronounced hypertrophy of the theca cells and interstitial cells, and the estrogenic activity of the ovary reappears.

WEISS inquired how much of the increase in diameter of the follicle is true growth. He pointed out that in the case of the eye much of the increase in diameter is due to the production of vitreous humor. To what extent does LH stimulate true growth, i.e., increase in number and size of cells, and to what extent does it merely stimulate production of follicular fluid? Quite different mechanisms are involved in the two instances, and it is essential that each effect be analyzed separately. BURNS then referred to some experiments on growth of ovarian follicles in the axolotl after hypophysectomy (Burns and Buyse, 1932). The animals were hypophysectomized as embryos. The ovaries developed quite well, and the egg cells entered the ovocyte stages and grew until they obtained a diameter of approximately 400 μ. At that stage the yolk granules are first laid down in the egg. Exactly at that stage all growth of egg cells ceases in hypophysectomized animals. Similarly, if adults are hypophysectomized when the ovary is full of mature eggs, all follicles containing mature eggs degenerate. All follicles containing yolk even in the smallest quantities degenerate. But those follicles which have not yet entered the stage of yolk formation persist in an apparently unchanged condition. In other words, the adult ovary after hypophysectomy reverts exactly to the stage of differentiation which the embryonic ovary is able to attain without the hypophysis. Something associated with the phenomenon of yolk metabolism is apparently involved in the arrest that occurs.

TONUTTI stated that the growth of follicles has been analyzed in his laboratory by Dr. Fetzer. In hypophysectomized rats, secondary follicles remain with a diameter of 150 μ. The nuclear size of the granulosa cells of these follicles is the same as in follicles of the same size in normal animals. When the follicles grow in the normal animal, the nuclear size first diminishes. After maturation of the follicle, the nuclear size of the granulosa cells increases and reaches its maximum at the time the granulosa cell is transformed into a lutein cell after rupture of the follicle.

After this diversion, Tonutti returned to the discussion of the interactions shown diagrammatically in Figure 12. After rupture of the mature follicle, the granulosa cells are transformed into the granulosa-lutein cells under the influence of LH (P). But the cells of the corpus luteum do not secrete progesterone until they are stimulated by the third gonadotrophin, namely, LTH (Q). Progesterone then acts back on the production of LTH (R) and LH (S) by the pituitary.

Gonadotrophins are not secreted in appreciable amounts before puberty. There remains the question concerning the factors which induce the pituitary to begin secretion of gonadotrophins at the time of puberty. Recall the case of the Leydig cell tumor in the five-and-a-half-year-old boy discussed earlier. Under the influence of the androgenic activity of the Leydig cell tumor, this boy reached a bone age of approximately twelve years. In this patient there was a detectable excretion of gonadotrophins in the urine, and true Leydig cells were present in both testes. Thus the precocious pseudo-puberty induced by androgens was already transforming into a true, but incomplete, precocious puberty. It appears that the pituitary begins to produce gonadotrophins automatically when the body has reached a certain degree of somatic maturation and not at a certain chronological age.

Just the opposite situation seems to be demonstrated by another patient, sixteen years of age (121 cm.), who lacked sexual development. This boy with secondary hypogonadism and dwarfism was treated for 3 years with chorionic gonadotrophin (LH activity). Within 3 years, complete sexual maturation occurred, and the patient increased 20 cm. in height and showed somatic maturation. When treatment was stopped after 3 years, he continued to grow, and gonadotrophins were excreted into the urine. The following interpretation seems indicated. The androgens produced by the Leydig cells under the influence of chorionic gonadotrophin induced somatic maturation. After a certain degree of maturation was reached, corresponding to the degree of maturation at the time of onset of puberty in a normal individual, the hypophysis began to secrete gonadotrophin.

108

hormones on enzyme systems either in vivo or in vitro. The best evidence that has been presented recently suggests that, whenever there is a change in enzymes due to hormone action, the effect is probably due to the action of the hormone on the synthesis of the enzyme protein rather than on the enzyme directly. WILLIER said that he supposed that hormones accelerate enzymatic action by perhaps acting as coenzymes. WEISS suggested that the hormone might also produce a structural change in the cell, which would permit the existing enzyme population to operate more efficiently per unit number of enzyme molecules. Of course, the actual enzyme efficiency depends on the probabilities of collision between the enzyme and the substrate. An ordered arrangement of the enzymes, if it is promoted by structural provisions in the cell, leads to the type of effect that Kollros had just described. SCHNEIDERMAN pointed out that in insects attention has been paid for a long time to changes in enzyme systems after hormonal treatment but that, more recently, attention has been focused on changes occurring in the intracellular structure after hormone administration. Recently Wigglesworth (unpublished) has shown that within a few hours after injection of the bloodsucking bug, *Rhodnius,* with the prothoracic gland hormone, ecdysone, the entire intracellular structure of the epidermal cells is changed. The endoplasmic reticulum looks very different, the mitochondria change in shape, etc. These events occur exceedingly rapidly and are paralleled by other changes—for example, by increased respiration, which is presumably a result of changes in mitochondria, and increased protein synthesis, which may be the result of changes in the endoplasmic reticulum. The suggestion has been made that ecdysone and possibly other hormones act by affecting intracellular permeability. Consider for a moment how a cell might regulate its metabolism. Certainly one way is to keep enzymes away from their substrates. One way to start reactions going is to bring enzymes into contact with their substrates. Thus some hormones may act by facilitating or restricting the access of enzymes to their substrates. Such mechanisms may be very important in the regulation of metabolism. WEISS agreed that it is possible that the primary change is in cellular organization and that any change in enzymatic activity is a secondary derivative of a more direct primary change. SCHNEIDERMAN added that this might be a change in mitochondrial permeability.

WEISS then inquired about the actual penetration of hormones into cells, as against surface action. Do they operate at the surface, and does this engender a change which propagates itself into the cell? Or do they actually enter the cell? Do certain hormones enter and others work on the outside? Perhaps the proteins behave differently from the steroids, which have lipid receptors in the cell surface.

WILLIER emphasized that an important aspect of the problem is how large molecules get into the circulation from the endocrine glands and, once in the circulation, how these large molecules are picked up by receptor organs. He emphasized also that they can leave and enter the circulation only through the walls of the capillaries, and he stressed, therefore, that the capillary wall may play an important role in the transfer of large molecules. WEISS, however, stated that it is not necessary to stress the role of capillary walls because hormones exert their actions in vitro when endocrine glands and receptors are cultured together. Capillaries add a complication only in vivo. He inquired whether WILLIER intended to imply that there is an actual screening of molecules at the capillary bed, which either retains the hormone in the circulation or allows it to enter the cells. If so, this cannot be the general situation because of the situation in vitro. The problem remains as already stated: Does the hormone merely affect the surface of the cell, and, as a consequence of this action, does the cell then proceed on its own? Or does the hormone actually enter? WILLIER stated that his working hypothesis was that, once the molecule gets into the capillary wall, is selectively picked up by it, the molecule is then bound to the cell membrane by some counterpart in the latter which it matches. Once this combination occurs, the cell membrane becomes active somehow or other in transforming the molecule into something simpler, which enables it to act within the enzyme-substrate system within the cell. This, in turn, results in the synthesis of a different product within the cell.

SCHNEIDERMAN thought that studies have been made in which labeled thyroxin is injected into an animal and subsequently the liver is homogenized and fractionated, to find out in what particular fraction the thyroxin is found. SEGAL objected that this gives information only about the location of the iodine. I^{131} may be lost rapidly from the thyroxin molecule and may well enter cells independently of the rest of the molecule. SCHNEIDERMAN stated that this necessitates the use of N^{15}-labeled thyroxin or something else. This would enable the investigator to find out the particular cell organelle in which the hormone is concentrated.

WEISS then inquired whether Dr. Price's enzyme studies with the Manns on the seminal vesicles give any indication of how the hormone works in mobilizing fructose. PRICE answered that Mann (1954) had reviewed the evidence that testicular hormone normally is essential for the production of fructose by accessory glands. He outlined a series of enzyme reactions which might be involved in the conversion of blood glucose to seminal fructose and postulated that alkaline phosphatases may facilitate fructose liberation from phosphofructose. Williams-Ashman and Banks (1954) found ketose reductase in fructose-producing glands and suggested that this enzyme might play a role in the conversion of glucose to fructose, with sorbitol as an intermediary. Hers (1957) has now confirmed this and has shown the second enzyme step in the transformation. But the way in which testicular androgen influences these enzyme systems in the accessory glands is not known.

MOOG then mentioned the work of Levine and Goldstein (1955) on the action of insulin on permeability. These authors eviscerated rats and then injected them with insulin and also with sugars which are not utilized by the muscles and other cells of the body. In this way, by separating the penetration from the utilization of sugars, they were able to demonstrate that insulin facilitates the penetration of these sugars just as much as it facilitates the penetration of glucose, which is utilized.

WEISS pointed out that there may be a selective receptor mechanism in the cell surface, placed there for recognition or rejection of a hormone molecule. Once accepted, perhaps this molecule can be passed down the line by the bucket brigade of active transport. Once inside the cell, it may have an entirely different activity. The mechanism of reception and the mechanism of action may even be connected with different parts of the molecule. The molecule may have a tag which is essential for its recognition and reception, and it may have another part which is instrumental to its proper function inside the cell. The part of the molecule that works inside the cell by promoting intracellular permeability may be different from the prosthetic group that causes the molecule to be accepted. MOOG pointed out that this certainty might be expected to be true in the case of proteins. WEISS suggested that perhaps the structural analogs of the steroids have a different spectrum of action, largely due to differential acceptance rather than to differential mechanisms of action, once they enter.

SCHNEIDERMAN inquired whether it is necessary to think of selective pickup of the hormone by the receptor organ. Is it not possible that it just happens that particular cells can use the hormone, whereas other cells, which also get it, cannot use it? WEISS answered that the labeling experiments demonstrate that the hormone is concentrated by a particular gland, and therefore it is selectively picked up. SCHNEIDERMAN agreed that this is certainly true of some hormones but that it cannot be assumed a priori that this is the way that all hormones behave.

WEISS concluded that nothing much is known about the real mode of action of any hormones. He inquired whether anything is known about how the hormones act in the production of cancer in response to steroid hormones. MÜHLBOCK replied that practically nothing is known on the cellular level. WEISS then asked about the action of hormones on the ground substances rather than on the cells. How does relaxin affect the mucopolysaccharides? GAILLARD replied that it affects them by acting on calcium exchange. WEISS then inquired whether this action occurs through the connective tissue cells or whether it is a direct attack on the ground substance. GAILLARD stated that it is generally assumed that its action is directly on the ground substance. He mentioned that gradients of action on the ground substance spreading from cells are not seen. The fact that has been observed is that the staining intensity of the ground substances is increased. It is assumed that the reaction is more intensive because smaller molecules are produced by depolymerization. WEISS asked whether the only studies of the reaction are those based on the Schiff reaction. He inquired whether some straight biochemical studies have been made. But, even then, only the product would be known and not the process behind the product.

WILLIER listed three hyotheses about hormone action based on a review of the literature: (1) the hormone acts by bringing about changes in concentration of enzymes in the tissues; (2) the hormone functions as a component of the enzyme system, as a coenzyme; (3) hormones act by having a direct or indirect effect on the acceleration and/or inhibition of enzyme systems. For example, in a recent study in vitro it was found that a particular homogenate could carry on the normal processes of synthesis of a hormone independently of the trophic hormone but that, when the latter was added, these processes were accelerated. SCHNEIDERMAN again remarked that another way that hormones may act is by changing intracellular permeability, thereby enabling an enzyme to come into contact with its substrate. WILLIER questioned whether this should be called "permeability," but WEISS reminded him that what is called "permeability" nowadays is becoming somewhat hazy. SCHNEIDERMAN continued by stating that inside the cells things are kept away from each other; there is compartmentation. One of the obvious way for nature to affect cellular activity is to allow compartments to mix. It is conceivable that this is one of the ways in which hormones can act. WEISS agreed and stated that this is what he implied in speaking of structural facilities for the reaction, but he stated that he had difficulty in visualizing how this could result in switching cellular activities into alternative courses. SCHNEIDERMAN replied that one compartment is affected in one case, another in another, etc.

WEISS suggested that this is only passing the buck from the cell as a whole to the cellular compartments. SCHNEIDERMAN defended his remarks by stating that the analysis is brought down at least one additional step to the intracellular level. WEISS replied that, even so, it is not brought down to the molecular level. How do hormones act to cause the cell to switch into a different line of differentiation? He called attention to the experiments of Fell and Mellanby (1953), in which the development of skin cells can be switched by treatment with vitamin A into a course which will produce slime and cilia. This is a model of events in the vagina under the cyclic action of steroid hormones. The two agents may act through a common point of attack. He pointed out that in his own laboratory it has been demonstrated that it takes only 15 minutes' exposure to vitamin A for the manifestation 5 days later of the switch in developmental fate (Weiss and James, 1954, 1955). The fate of the whole protoplasmic system has been changed rather dramatically by a very short exposure, which is definitely, as far as indirect evidence is concerned, confined to the surface. It does not penetrate. Perhaps these experiments provide a model of hormone action. GAILLARD inquired whether the concentrations used in these experiments are not exceedingly high in comparison with the concentrations of hormones. WEISS replied that they are not high in his experiments. The concentration is 1/10,000 vitamin A in 5 per cent alcohol for 15 minutes. Thereafter the cells are completely washed. The cells that show the effect later are not the same cells that were treated, but are about the third-generation progeny. Thus the level of vitamin A falls below that characteristic of normal plasma.

SCHNEIDERMAN suggested that the enzyme systems that have been studied intensively are mostly those concerned with mobilizing energy. These have proved exceedingly uninteresting, as far as hormone action is concerned. The reason that analysis of hormone action has not progressed effectively on the molecular level is that hormones affect many synthetic reactions, and in such cases the enzymes involved are unknown. WEISS agreed and reminded the group that statements exist in the literature of embryology to the effect that "specific enzymes, or the reactions catalyzed by them, control such processes as determination, morphogenesis, or differentiation. So far this has not been proven for any enzyme" (Boell, 1955, p. 548).

SCHNEIDERMAN then suggested that perhaps, before going immediately from the response of the entire cell to the molecular mechanisms involved, some idea concerning what happens to the ultrastructure of cells shortly after hormone treatment should be obtained by the use of the electron microscope. WEISS answered that he has been doing this for several years and that useful information has resulted but that such an approach is leading down only one order of magnitude, which is still far removed from the molecular level. The point to emphasize is that almost nothing is known about the mode of action of the hormone at its terminal point, by which its action is gauged. How the hormone furnishes a signal to which the receptor can respond is not known. One of the great absurdities of modern research is the discrepancy between the amount of work that is being done at the end of purification, crystallization, and identification of hormones versus the shortage of work on the action of hormones. Perhaps it is because the latter task is so difficult or because no one sees a way to attack it.

MARTINOVITCH inquired whether the hormone activates the substrate, i.e., whether it acts as an enzyme. He pointed out that Tonutti feels that hormones are not used up in the chain of reactions following their administration. WEISS stated that this raises the question as to how much of the hormone can be recovered after it has acted. TONUTTI mentioned that Selye (1949) reduced the size of a receptor organ to see whether the response of the reduced receptor would be greater to a given amount of hormone than in the normal situation. He found it to be no greater. Naturally, such an experiment would be valid only if all the administered hormone were accumulated by the receptor organ. If the hormone is distributed equally over the entire body, reduction in size of a small receptor by half would have no significance. WEISS felt that this approach is too indirect to be useful. He inquired whether anyone has ever extirpated a thyroid from a fully stimulated animal, transplanted it to a hypophysectomized animal, and demonstrated the escape of residual thyrotrophic hormone from the graft in an amount sufficient to stimulate host thyroids. Assuming that the thyroid does concentrate thyrotrophic hormone and not degrade it, can it be gotten out of the thyroid again by grinding up that thyroid and putting it into a hypophysectomized animal to see whether there is at least a temporary flaring-up of host thyroid activity?

GAILLARD reviewed an experiment of his which is somewhat like the experiment suggested by Weiss. He added parathormone to a culture medium in a given concentration and allowed it to act on bone tissue, which underwent resorption as a consequence of this hormone action. He then took some of the fluid in which this action had occurred and placed it in a new container along with another piece of bone, which, in turn, underwent resorption. WEISS pointed out that this merely means that hormone is still present in the medium; it does not mean that it has, or has not, entered the receptor apparatus. TONUTTI again emphasized, as he had done earlier, that there is a great difference from one organ to another. When thyrotrophic hormone is incubated with fresh tissue, it is inactivated, but it is not used up in the usual sense of the term. WEISS answered that at least it is not being recirculated; it is lost as far as additional activity is concerned. Is this an accurate model of what happens in the body? SCHNEIDERMAN stated that if a trophic hormone is to be able to regulate some gland, it just cannot sit around for a long time. It has to be there to exert its effect, and, if its effect is to be stopped, it has to be broken down. WEISS suggested that the hormone as a whole may not be the catalyst. The part of the molecule that acts as a catalyst may not be used up, but it may then be unrecognizable because it has lost its specific tag of recognition, once this part of the molecule has been released from the total hormone molecule.

MOOG pointed out that steroid hormones are metabolized very rapidly. SEGAL stated that they may be metabolized in the liver rather than at their site of action. WEISS emphasized that if they are destroyed in the liver, they must first come out of their site of action, and this would provide indirect evidence that they are only passing through receptor organs. KOLLROS stated that the ones which are destroyed in the liver may simply be the ones which failed to reach the receptors. GAILLARD mentioned that ACTH is extremely labile in pure plasma. Within 24 hours after it is added to plasma, its activity is literally absent because of disintegration of the active substance.

BURNS emphasized that the case may be very different not only for different end organs but for different types of hormones. Exactly opposite to the case described by Tonutti, where a part of a receptor does not grow to any larger size after the rest of it has been removed, although it is exposed to the full concentration of the hormone, is the situation in which compensatory hypertrophy of one ovary occurs after removal of the other one. This has always been explained on the basis of the fact that, with one ovary gone, the other somehow or other profits by the excess gonadotrophin which is in circulation. WEISS pointed out that O. M. Robertson (unpublished) had demonstrated the same response for one testis of a trout following removal of the other one. MARTINOVITCH mentioned that the adrenal responds similarly. But WEISS then emphasized that Robertson's trout were said to have also responded when hypophysectomized. KOLLROS then mentioned that this is the old pattern of the crab claw in regeneration. WEISS noted that he had quoted a large amount of literature of this kind in his article on specificity and growth control (Weiss, 1955). Such reactions are scattered throughout the entire animal kingdom. This is actually what led to his hypothesis

119

of a steady state for the total volume of any organ system, irrespective of how it is divided into pairs of organs, scattered islets, or what not. It is the total mass that is under control. In the case of the testes of the trout, there would be a direct action between the testis on the left and the one on the right through the humoral system of the body. If one is removed, the other enlarges. In addition to such a mechanism acting according to the principles developed by Weiss and Kavanau (1957), there is apparently a second system of growth control involving the pituitary and the production of gonadotrophins. WEISS suggested that in all endocrine glands both mechanisms are probably demonstrable. He raised a question about the old Halsted law of transplantation, which states that if a supernumerary organ is added by transplantation, it is better to get rid of the counterpart first and thus to reduce the total mass of that particular organ system. He inquired whether this also holds true for the endocrine system. GAILLARD answered in the affirmative, except for the anterior pituitary. MARTINOVITCH stated that the anterior pituitary can be transplanted in any amount and will take. As many as ten have been transplanted successfully.

MÜHLBOCK stated that, after unilateral ovariectomy in mice, the remaining ovary shows compensatory hypertrophy (Mühlbock and Boot, 1956). As a measure of the function of the remaining ovary, the number of ova released at ovulation is counted. On the average, 5 ova per ovary are found in the normal animal. After unilateral ovariectomy the remaining ovary produces double that number. If an additional ovary is implanted subcutaneously either at the time of unilateral ovariectomy or some weeks later, compensatory hypertrophy of the ovary *in situ* is not inhibited. If it is postulated that the hypophysis releases only a limited amount of gonadotrophic hormone, it may be concluded that this hormone is effective only on the ovary *in situ*. The gonadotrophic hormone is effective only on the subcutaneous ovarian graft after extirpation of the remaining ovary *in situ*. WEISS stated that a similar kind of observation has been made recently in fish by Peters in Tübingen (1955, personal communication).

WEISS then inquired about what happens immediately after hypophysectomy. MÜHLBOCK replied that in the rat with ovaries *in situ* a continuous state of pseudo-pregnancy is found after removal of the pituitary gland from the sella to the kidney (Everett, 1954, 1956). This means that, after its transplantation to another site than the sella, i.e., away from the hypothalamus, the hypophysis produces predominantly luteotrophic hormone. During the estrous cycle of the normal animal the hypophysis produces no luteotrophic hormone. Corpora lutea are formed at ovulation, but they do not produce progesterone.

WEISS inquired whether the number of eggs produced by the two ovaries is approximately the same. MÜHLBOCK answered in the affirmative. He said that they make a routine practice of transferring fertilized eggs and practically always find the same number. BURNS recalled that, in the original experiments on unilateral ovariectomy mentioned earlier, the remaining ovary, after removal of the other one, always matures approximately twice the normal number of follicles for that ovary. MÜHLBOCK stressed the importance of the use of pure-bred strains for experiments of this type. GAILLARD suggested that the site of implantation is of importance as well as the strain. If the ovary of the mouse is transplanted together with its extra-coelomic cavity, a successful graft is obtained, whereas if the ovary is grafted alone and no free surface is provided, the graft does not take. MÜHLBOCK disagreed and stated that in their experiments the results were the same in either case. BURNS said that he knew nothing about the situation in the adult but that, in the case of the embryonic ovary of the rat, a small, free space is essential around it in order to obtain survival and good differentiation, just as Gaillard had described.

GAILLARD mentioned that, when suprarenal glands are grafted into the brain, they take but do not function until the moment the animals are adrenalectomized.

KOLLROS then discussed the field of amphibian metamorphosis in relation to the problem of the mode of attack of hormones. It is obvious that before the thyroid acts, the pituitary must act by producing thyrotrophic hormone. What it is that induces the pituitary to increase its production of thyrotrophic hormone at a particular time and thus to bring about the precipitous events of metamorphosis is not known. Etkin (1936, 1939) demonstrated, by transplanting the thyroid gland adjacent to the pituitary gland, that the pituitary produces thyrotrophic hormone a great deal earlier than the climactic events of metamorphosis indicate. A very much accelerated metamorphosis results. It is presumed that thyrotrophic hormone from the pituitary gland reaches the adjacent thyroid gland by diffusion, thereby activating it. The histologic response of the thyroid gland confirms this. Presumably, the amount of TSH released by the pituitary at the early stages studied is insufficient, when diluted in the circulation, to have an effect upon the thyroid gland at its usual site. There is no evidence to indicate how much earlier the pituitary might be producing and releasing TSH.

Questions have been raised concerning the onset of reactivity of the tissues to the thyroid hormone. It is known that in embryonic stages the tissues are not reactive. However, some studies by Moser (1950) indicate that a whole series of tissues in the tadpole show a response at about the time feeding begins. This takes place in the *Rana pipiens* tadpole at about a length of 10 cm. A particular cell type in the brain which eventually responds to thyroid hormone does not become reactive until the tadpole is about 30 mm. long (Kollros and McMurray, 1956). Thus different tissues become responsive at somewhat different levels of development. WEISS inquired how this responsiveness is tested. KOLLROS answered that resorption of the tail is studied by measurements on the shortening tail. WEISS asked whether this begins at the 10-mm. stage. KOLLROS answered that it does if a great deal of thyroid hormone is given. If thyroid hormone is added in substantial concentration to the medium in which the tadpole is swimming, starting at the time the tadpole is 8 mm. long, i.e., while it is still embryonic and utilizing its yolk, a shortening of the tail can be detected about the time it gets to be 10 or 11 mm. This is a specific reaction to thyroxin, just as is stimulation of the hind limbs. The hind limbs cannot be stimulated until after the limb buds have developed to a certain point. WEISS mentioned that he had less confidence in the reduction of something as a criterion for hormone activity than in a positive criterion. KOLLROS mentioned that Moser also used the loss of the beak as a criterion of response. This again is a specific reaction occurring at no other time than at metamorphosis. WEISS inquired whether jawbones form also, or whether the reaction is simply the loss of something. KOLLROS stated that Moser did not carry his experiments far enough to know. He found that all four or five of his test structures showed the onset of tissue reactivity to thyroxin at about the same time. The embryo is apparently unreactive to thyroxin until the 8-mm. stage, and subsequently, in a given sequence, certain tissues become reactive to the hormones.

There are special differences between urodeles and anurans. Certain reactions that are considered to be metamorphic in the frog are not metamorphic in salamanders. The corneal reflex is one of these, since it develops in the hypophysectomized and thus non-metamorphosing salamander, whereas in the frog it depends completely upon thyroid hormone and the metamorphic changes in the eye and brain (Kollros, 1942). Likewise, the pupillary response first appears at metamorphosis (Stone, 1930). Thus behavior may be listed as a functional index of hormone activity, and changes in behavior are involved in the whole complex of changes called, collectively, "metamorphosis." Thus in the eye of the salamander one behavioral response appears to be metamorphically limited, the other is not. In the frog both of them depend upon metamorphosis.

Thus in amphibian larvae certain tissues are responsive to thyroid hormone, while others are not. Those which are responsive exhibit either progressive development, such as the hind limbs beyond a certain stage, or regressive development, as in the case of the tail, the beaks, and, in the salamanders, the tail fin, if not the entire tail. Some of the structures which show progressive development do so because of the direct action of the thyroid hormone (Kollros and Kaltenbach, 1952; Kaltenbach, 1953*a*, *b*; Kollros and McMurray, 1956). Other changes are clearly the results of indirect hormonal action. Helff (1928), for example, demonstrated that the modification of the skin over the tympanic membrane depends upon influences emanating from the annular tympanic cartilage whose own prior changes are under the control of thyroid hormone.

How can it be demonstrated that some tissue is directly responsive to hormone? This can be ascertained by transplantation of small pellets which contain thyroxin. The first work of this kind was that of Hartwig (1940). He soaked pellets of agar in strong solutions of thyroxin and then implanted the pellets in the tail fins of salamanders. The response consisted of a regression of the fin, an indentation of the fin margin at the level of the implant. Pellets of agar alone do not produce this result. Kollros (1943) implanted thyroxin-soaked agar pellets into the hindbrain of the frog tadpole. The result was a precocious development of the hindbrain center, which is responsible for the corneal reflex. This is a local effect on a behavioral feature. The performance of the reflex thus occurred in larval stages a great deal earlier than it would have normally. Since the period of larval development is divided into an extensive series of well-marked stages (Taylor and Kollros, 1946), the extent of this temporary disharmony can be indicated very clearly. Thyroxin-agar pellets liberate their hormone very quickly, so that local effects are frequently masked by generalized effects resulting from the rapid accumulation of thyroxin in the blood. Well-compacted pellets of cholesterol and thyroxin combined in a ratio of 4 to 1 are better for this purpose, since such a pellet, if about 0.5 mm. in diameter and less than 0.2 mm. thick, liberates its hormone over a period of a week or longer. Although generalized hormonal stimulation is not avoided, it is much less exaggerated than with agar-base pellets, and the striking local effects are generally easily distinguishable from the modest generalized ones (Kollros and Kaltenbach, 1952).

There has been a serious controversy, mainly between certain American and European investigators, concerning an interpretation of meta-morphic mechanisms. Moser (1950), for example, apparently assumes that particular metamorphic events require particular threshold levels of thyroid hormone to be reached or exceeded before they occur. By contrast, Etkin (1955) asserts that any concentration of thyroid hor-mone adequate to bring about any of the metamorphic reactions is adequate to bring about all of them, given enough time for the action. There is now sufficient evidence to rule against the latter idea in favor of the former, i.e., in favor of the idea of several specific thresholds. Geigy (1941) reported no concentrations below one part in two billion and stated that this is ineffective. Allen (1938) likewise stated that this concentration is ineffective. Their negative results apparently stemmed from their use of normal tadpoles, in which the intrinsic hormone pro-duction and release mask the modest influence of thyroid hormone in low concentration. In his own recent experiments the highest concen-tration used was one part in one billion (1 μg/liter) in the culture water. This level is sufficient, for hypophysectomized and thus effective-ly thyroidless larvae, for all events of metamorphosis through develop-ment of the legs, perforation of the operculum and emergence of the forelegs, development of skin glands, and substantial loss or resorption of oral fringes, tail fin, and axial structures of the tail. With concen-trations of thyroxin only 1 per cent as strong as this, certain metamor-phic events can still be stimulated. The development of the hind limb, for example, seems for a time to be independent of the thyroid gland, since, in hypophysectomized tadpoles, it proceeds to the level of the normal stage VI–VII tadpole. Then development terminates until stim-ulated by the introduction of hormones. Stage VII is the stage at which one digit of the foot is separated from the common primordium of the other digits. Treatment with low concentrations of thyroxin will stimu-late further differentiation of the leg to the stage of two, three, four, or five toes. Which of these stages is reached depends mainly upon two things: the concentration of added thyroxin and the temperature. If the concentration is correct to bring about the development of three digits, further treatment at the same hormone concentration will bring about no additional change, even though such animals may be treated for an additional 12 months. However, if the temperature is elevated by sev-eral degrees or if the hormone concentration is increased slightly during this time, some additional metamorphic progress is achieved, i.e., four or five toes may be produced. Temperature involves either the sensitivity of the responding tissues or their ability to respond at all (Kollros, 1956). It has been known for a long time that cold temperatures completely inhibit metamorphosis. If larvae at the room temperatures of summer respond slightly to a given concentration of thyroxin, they may fail to respond at 17° C. Or, if they still respond at 17°, they may no longer do so at 15°. Thus, speaking of hypophysectomized tadpoles treated only with external sources of d-l-thyroxin in the dose range of 0.01 to 1.0 μg/liter, the following elements which affect metamorphosis must be kept in mind: (*a*) time of onset of tissue reactivity to thyroxin; (*b*) different thresholds for response by different tissues (remembering, further, that some responding tissues at first have high thresholds and later lower ones); (*c*) different rates of response of different tissues at any given effective hormone concentration; (*d*) influence of temperature levels upon either *b* or *c* or both.

The studies of Kollros and McMurray (1955, 1956) serve to illustrate points *a* and *b*. The mesencephalic V nucleus cells in *Rana pipiens* apparently cannot respond to high concentrations of thyroxin by growth of both nucleus and cell body prior to stage III (length of about 30 mm.). They respond slightly in stages III–IV and more completely at stage V, though they are probably not yet fully responsive even then (see Kollros and McMurray, 1956, pp. 3–6 and Table 1). When metamorphosis is stimulated in hypophysectomized animals with thyroxin concentrations barely adequate to bring the larvae to the stage of forelimb emergence (stage XX) or slightly beyond, many tissues change (skin glands develop, molting occurs, legs develop fully, the operculum perforates, the extrinsic ocular muscles enlarge, the gape of the jaws may increase), but such hormone concentrations appear to be inadequate to stimulate growth of the cells of the mesencephalic V nucleus (see Kollros and McMurray, 1956, pp. 14-15 and Fig. 6). Thus these unique, easily recognizable cells of the optic tectum can be seen to be readily stimulated to enlarge by high concentrations of hormone at stage V, but, if metamorphosis is stimulated over a long period of time by low concentrations of hormone, the cells remain small, even though they begin to enlarge in the stage XIV–XVI interval. Their failure to enlarge by the time stage XX is reached clearly implies that they are stimulated only by hormone concentrations substantially higher than those required to bring about the other metamorphic changes enumerated. They are highly reactive cells, but only with relatively high concentrations of thyroxin.

One additional feature which might have been considered as item *e* above is the rate at which release of thyroid hormone occurs in the normally metamorphosing animal. There is no assay for it prior to stage VII. Apparently, it increases very slowly at first, as indicated by the progress of limb development after stage VII. Its concentration then appears to increase more rapidly, and even precipitously, at or just prior to metamorphic climax. There is then evidence that the concentration declines, but just how far is not evident. Studies by Barch (1953) have yielded interesting information on the rate of oxygen utilization by skin at different stages and on the responsiveness of the skin to thyroxin. The first index of increase in thyroid hormone is the differentiation and growth of the legs, which, though highly sensitive to the hormone, at first respond to it very slowly. Skin glands next develop. The thinning of the skin window and shortening of the tail are both relatively insensitive indicators of hormone concentration, but, once adequate concentration of hormone has been reached, they respond rapidly. In hypophysectomized animals, however, it is possible to achieve a very delicate balance of hormone concentration such that thinning of the skin window does occur but rupture does not. If dosage levels are exactly right, the spiracle disappears, and regression of the skin window area by erosion from the edge of the spiracle may go on, being restricted to the left side of the body. By similar control of dosage, regression of the tail may be stretched out over a period of several months rather than over some 6-10 days (Kollros, unpublished).

The feedback mechanism remains to be discussed, i.e., the influence of the thyroid hormone upon the pituitary gland. There is a substantial reduction in the thyroid hormone content of the blood after metamorphic climax. Is this reduction controlled by inhibition of TSH output by the pituitary? There is no evidence of such an effect during the long buildup period terminating after forelimb emergence. Is the pituitary, in fact, responsive to thyroid hormone at this time? It is responsive to rather large doses of the hormone. If a large thyroxin-cholesterol pellet is implanted in a normal tadpole, a rapid spurt of metamorphic development is recorded, beginning 2 or 3 days after implantation. If the pellet size is gauged correctly, there will be too little hormone to bring about the climactic phase of metamorphosis, and, after a few days of rapid change, the rate of change will decrease and may come to a complete halt. The tadpole may then remain unchanged for 3, 6, or 9 weeks, even for as long as 10 months (rarely). This block to metamorphosis is interpreted as thyroxin-induced inhibition of TSH output, the recovery from which may be rapid or very slow. Once metamorphic changes begin again, the course of metamorphosis proceeds normally. The metamorphic stasis indicates that the pituitary gland is sensitive to thyroid hormone but that ordinarily inhibitive concentrations of the hormone are not achieved prior to metamorphic climax.

WEISS emphasized the value of the metamorphic process as a tool for the analysis of the action of thyroid hormone on the tissues. There is one large cell on each side of the hindbrain of all amphibians and fish, called "Mauthner's cell." This is one huge brain cell. There is only one on each side of the animal, characterized by its enormous nucleolus, large nucleus, and very large cell body. This cell is surrounded by other large cells, the ones that Kollros mentioned. As metamorphosis proceeds, this cell regresses; its regression has been studied in *Xenopus* by Stefanelli (1950). After metamorphosis, it can no longer be recognized, so its ultimate fate is unknown. Weiss and Rossetti (1951) studied this cell under a variety of experimental conditions and also by implantation of thyroid directly into the ventricle against the area containing Mauthner's cell, so that the latter could be exposed to the direct influence of thyroxin from a localized source. The implantation of fresh thyroid stimulates an enormous increase in mitotic activity in the ependyma of that area; neither boiled thyroid nor any other control gland exerts this action. How this effect is brought about is unknown. The volume of all the nuclei of the large cells in this area increases within a few days. By contrast, Mauthner's cell regresses. One cell thus emancipates itself in its response from all the rest of the population and reacts entirely differently from the rest of them. This certainly pinpoints selectivity, even within a population of nerve cells! If this type of reaction is followed up in such a way as to determine how this cell differs metabolically, structurally, etc., from its neighbors, some clue concerning the point of attack of thyroxin may be provided.

Thyroxin also has a striking action on muscle. Recall that muscle consists of sarcomeres and that there are isotropic parts (I) and anisotropic parts (A). According to present electronmicrography, actin fibrils run clear through the muscle fiber, whereas myosin fibrils are short, stubby pieces found only in the anisotropic zones associated with, and probably wrapped around, the actin fibrils. At metamorphosis in urodele larvae, most of the muscles remain entirely intact, but the gill muscles disappear when thyroxin appears. The I bands of the gill muscles are completely hydrolyzed and dissolved out, while the A bands float around as loose plates of myosin filaments, which finally become secondarily dissolved. Here again there is a very neat chemical fractionation of tissue components by thyroxin. Another striking effect is on the basement lamella of the skin of amphibian larvae. This membrane separates the connective tissue from the epidermis, which, in urodeles, contains large glandular cells, the Leydig cells, and smaller basal cells and cover cells. During metamorphosis this basement membrane is perforated

127

under the action of thyroxin (Weiss and Ferris, 1954*a, b, c, d*). It is invaded very much like the invasion of germinal cords through the basement membrane of the ovary. Nests of epidermal cells which penetrate the basement membrane form the subcutaneous glands. The Leydig cells disappear. Again there is a definite local effect on the basement membrane. At this time the invasion of connective tissue cells into the microstructural lamellae of the basement membrane can be seen electronmicrographically; they enter along cleavage lines forming the dermis. This can be done only by cells dissolving the ground substance that holds the membrane together. Either these cells develop at this time a hyaluronidase or some other enzyme which becomes activated by thyroxin, which seems unlikely, or the ground substance of the basement membrane becomes susceptible to the enzymatic action of these cells at this time, which seems more likely. Otherwise they could not invade. This links up with what was said earlier about the action of relaxin on the ground substances and perhaps even with the invasiveness of tumors, cancers, etc. There probably is a common denominator somewhere, and the behavior of the basement membrane of amphibian larvae in response to thyroxin may offer an unusually favorable point of attack for an understanding of the molecular mechanism of action of the thyroxin molecule. WEISS considers metamorphosis of amphibians to be a gold mine for analyses of this type.

KOLLROS recalled that Kollros and Kaltenbach (1952) reported observations on the local metamorphosis of the skin. Thyroxin-cholesterol pellets implanted under the skin produced neat patches of metamorphosed skin surrounded by larval skin. He showed a hypophysectomized animal treated with thyroxin alone at a concentration of 0.6 μg/liter. It had developed to stage XIII and possessed rather well-developed glandular ridges. Control animals at this stage have no trace of skin glands, let alone patent glands. He showed another animal which had been treated similarly but which had developed to stage XX—the stage of forelimb emergence—before fixation. It exhibited a very marked junction between the skin of the tail base and the more dorsal skin, which shows adult pigment spots and which will persist, and the more ventral skin, which retains larval characteristics and pigmentation and which will disappear with the rest of the tail. The distinction is much clearer than in the normal animal at stage XX. In section, glands and a stratum corneum can be seen in the dorsal skin; the ventral skin lacks glands and retains the larval arrangement of layers of cells. Incidentally, the corneal reflex was elicitable from the treated animal for over 2 months, whereas normally this reflex is elicitable only 4 or 5 days prior to forelimb emergence. WEISS mentioned that in the normal metamorphosis of the European salamander, *Salamandra maculosa,* this zone is very sharply defined as it moves up on the tail. With the aid of the electron miscroscope it is possible to distinguish one cell on one side of the line that has metamorphosed and another cell on the opposite side which has remained larval in type. SCHNEIDERMAN inquired concerning the fates of the larval cells. KOLLROS and WEISS answered that they are resorbed.

KOLLROS then added a few comments concerning Mauthner's cell. A thyroxin-cholesterol pellet was placed lateral to the medulla oblongata just anterior to the level of this special cell. Although the distance for diffusion of the hormone is considerable, there was probably less diffusion into the blood stream than in the experiments of Weiss and Rossetti (1951). Pesetsky and Kollros (1956) presented a table of nuclear sizes of non-Mauthnerian cells on the two sides of the hindbrain, confirming the conclusions of Weiss and Rossetti, insofar as stimulation of cell growth by thyroxin is concerned. The cells on the side of the implant became significantly larger than those on the opposite side, far removed from the source of the hormone. The nuclei of Mauthner's cells on the side of the implant were reduced insignificantly $(P = 0.33)$ compared with those of the opposite side. However, if the six specimens which had proceeded to stage XX with emergent forelimbs are selected from the nineteen that were treated, the Mauthnerian nuclei on the side of the implant are then found to be significantly smaller than those on the opposite side (164 μ^2 versus 196 μ^2, $P = 0.02$). The conclusion was reached that involution of Mauthner's cells requires either high concentrations of thyroid hormone locally for several days or high concentrations of the hormone locally in addition to earlier degeneration of lateral-line nerve centers or tail motor centers as a result of a relatively high hormone concentration in the general circulation. Apparently, one or more of these conditions did not obtain in the thirteen animals which did not proceed to the stage of forelimb emergence. Thus Mauthner's cell reacts by involution to the thyroid hormone, while other small and intermediate-sized cell types nearby react by growing, as pointed out by Weiss and Rossetti.

129

References

ADLER, L. 1914. Metamorphosestudien an Batrachierlarven. I. Exstirpation endokriner Drüsen. A. Exstirpation der Hypophyse. Roux' Arch. Entw.-Mech., **39**:21–45.

ALLEN, B. M. 1938. The endocrine control of amphibian metamorphosis. Biol. Rev., **13**:1–19.

BACHMAN, C., COLLIP, J. B., and SELYE, H. 1936. Further studies of sex skin reactions in *Macaca mulatta*. Proc. Soc. Exper. Biol. & Med., **33**:549–51.

BACHMANN, R. 1954. Die Nebenniere. Handb. mikr. Anat. Menschen, Vol. **6**, Part 5. Berlin: Springer-Verlag.

BARCH, S. H. 1953. Oxygen consumption of normal and thyroxin-stimulated *Rana pipiens* skin. Physiol. Zoöl., **26**:223–31.

BARNICOT, N. A. 1948. The local action of the parathyroid and other tissues on bone in intracerebral grafts. J. Anat., **82**:233–48.

BELL, P. H. 1954. Purification and structure of β-corticotropin. J. Am. Chem. Soc., **76**:5565–67.

BENIRSCHKE, K., BLOCH, E., and HERTIG, A. T. 1956. Concerning the function of the fetal zone of the human adrenal gland. Endocrinology, **58**:598–625.

BILLINGHAM, R. E., BRENT, L., and MEDAWAR, P. B. 1956. Quantitative studies on tissue transplantation immunity. III. Actively acquired tolerance. Phil. Tr. Roy. Soc. London, B, **239**:357–414.

BILLINGHAM, R. E., LAMPKIN, G. H., MEDAWAR, P. B., and WILLIAMS, H. L. 1952. Tolerance to homografts, twin diagnosis, and the freemartin condition in cattle. Heredity, **6**:201–12.

BISSONNETTE, T. H. 1924. The development of the reproductive ducts and canals in the free-martin with comparison of the normal. Am. J. Anat., **33**:267–345.

BLOCH, E., BENIRSCHKE, K., and ROSEMBERG, E. 1956. C_{19} steroids, 17 α-hydroxycorticosterone and a sodium retaining factor in human fetal adrenal glands. Endocrinology, **58**:626–33.

BLOUNT, R. F. 1935. Size relationships as influenced by pituitary rudiment implantation and extirpation in the urodele embryo. J. Exper. Zoöl., **70**:131–85.

BOELL, E. J. 1955. Energy exchange and enzyme development during embryogenesis. *In:* Analysis of development, ed. B. H. WILLIER, P. WEISS, and V. HAMBURGER, Sec. VIII, pp. 520–55. Philadelphia and London: W. B. Saunders Co.

BOOT, L. M., and MÜHLBOCK, O. 1953. Transplantations of ova in mice. Acta physiol. et pharmacol. neerl., **3**:133–36.

BOUIN, P., and ANCEL, P. 1903. Sur la signification de la glande interstitielle du testicule embryonnaire. Compt. rend. Soc. biol., **55**:1682–84.

BULLOUGH, W. S. 1950. Epidermal mitotic activity in the adult female mouse. J. Endocrinol., **6**:340–49.

BURNS, R. K. 1942. Hormones and the growth of the parts of the urinogenital apparatus in mammalian embryos. Cold Spring Harbor Symp. Quant. Biol., 10:27–34.

————. 1950. Sex transformation in the opossum: some new results and a retrospect. Arch. anat. micr. et morphol. expér., 39:467–81.

————. 1955. Urinogenital system. *In:* Analysis of development, ed. B. H. WILLIER, P. WEISS, and V. HAMBURGER, Sec. VII, chap. 6, pp. 462–91. Philadelphia and London: W. B. Saunders Co.

————. 1956a. Hormones versus constitutional factors in the growth of embryonic sex primordia in the opossum. Am. J. Anat., 98:35–67.

————. 1956b. Transformation du testicule embryonnaire de l'opossum en ovotestis ou en "ovaire" sous l'action de l'hormone femelle, le dipropionate d'œstradiol. Arch. anat. micr. et morphol. expér., 45:173–202.

BURNS, R. K., and BUYSE, A. 1932. Effects of hypophysectomy on the reproductive system of salamanders. Anat. Rec., 51:333–59.

BUTENANDT, A., and KARLSON, P. 1954. Über die Isolierung eines Metamorphose-Hormons der Insekten in kristallisierter Form. Ztschr. Naturforsch., 9b:389–91.

CAIRNS, J. M., and SAUNDERS, J. W., JR. 1954. The influence of embryonic mesoderm on the regional specification of epidermal derivatives in the chick. J. Exper. Zoöl., 127:221–48.

CARPENTER, E. 1942. Differentiation of chick embryo thyroids in tissue culture. J. Exper. Zoöl., 89:407–31.

CASE, J. F. 1952. Adrenal cortical–anterior pituitary relationships during embryonic life. Ann. New York Acad. Sc., 55:147–58.

CHANG, C. Y. 1955. Hormonal influences on sex differentiation in the toad, *Bufo americanus*. Anat. Rec., 123:467–85.

CHANG, C. Y., and WITSCHI, E. 1955a. Independence of adrenal hyperplasia and gonadal masculinization in the experimental adrenogenital syndrome of frogs. Endocrinology, 56:597–605.

————. 1955b. Breeding of sex-reversed males of *Xenopus laevis* Daudin. Proc. Soc. Exper. Biol. & Med., 89:150–52.

CHANG, H. 1951. Grafts of parathyroid and other tissues to bone. Anat. Rec., 111:23–47.

CHIEFFI, G. 1952. Sull'organogenesi dell'interrenale e della medulla della gonade in *Torpedo ocellata* e in *Scylliorhinus canicula*. Pubbl. staz. zool. Napoli, 23: 186–200.

COURRIER, R. 1951. Contribution à l'endocrinologie de la thyroïde. Acta endocrinol., 7:54–59.

DEMUTH, F. 1933. Über die Züchtung von Schilddrüsenzellen in vitro. Arch. f. exper. Zellforsch., 13:329–70.

DOMM, L. V. 1939. Modifications in sex and secondary sexual characters in birds. *In:* Sex and internal secretions, chap. v, pp. 227–327. 2d ed. Baltimore: Williams & Wilkins Co.

DOSSEL, W. E. 1954. An experimental study of the structural and functional development of the thyroid of the chick embryo. Unpublished doctoral dissertation, Johns Hopkins University, Baltimore.

————. 1957. Effects of depletion and substitution of perivesicular mesenchyme upon the development of the thyroid primordium. J. Elisha Mitchell. Sc. Soc., 73:244.

Dossel, W. E. 1958. Regulation of growth and function of thyroid tissue in chick embryos bearing implants of thyroid vesicles. Anat. Rec., **130**:293–94.

Du Vigneaud, V. 1956. Hormones of the posterior pituitary gland: oxytocin and vasopressin. Harvey Lect. 1954–55, pp. 1–26.

Ebeling, A. H. 1924. Action de l'épithélium thyroïdien en culture pure sur la croissance des fibroblastes. Compt. rend. Soc. biol., **90**:1449–50.

Échalier, G. 1954. Recherches expérimentales sur le rôle de "l'organe Y" dans la mue de *Carcinus moenas* (L.), crustacé décapode. Compt. rend. Acad. sc., **238**:523–25.

———. 1955. Rôle de l'organe Y dans le déterminisme de la mue de *Carcinides (Carcinus) moenas* L. (crustacés décapodes); expériences d'implantation. *Ibid.*, **240**:1581–83.

Engfeldt, B. 1950. Studies on parathyroidal function in relation to hormonal influences and dietetic conditions. Acta endocrinol., Suppl., **6**:1–118.

Engfeldt, B., and Zetterström, R. 1954. Biophysical and chemical investigation on bone tissue in experimental hyperparathyroidism. Endocrinology, **54**:506–15.

Etkin, W. 1934. The phenomena of anuran metamorphosis. II. E. Oxygen consumption during normal metamorphosis. Physiol. Zoöl., **7**:129–48.

———. 1936. A thyrotropic field surrounding the immature pituitary of the tadpole. Proc. Soc. Exper. Biol. & Med., **34**:508–12.

———. 1939. A thyrotropic field effect in the tadpole. Part 1. J. Exper. Zoöl., **82**:463–95.

———. 1955. Metamorphosis. *In:* Analysis of development, ed. B. H. Willier, P. Weiss, and V. Hamburger, Sec. XII, pp. 631–63. Philadelphia and London: W. B. Saunders Co.

Everett, J. W. 1954. Luteotrophic function of autographs of the rat hypophysis. Endrocrinology, **54**:685–90.

———. 1956. Functional corpora lutea maintained for months by autographs of rat hypophyses. *Ibid.*, **58**:786–96.

Fabbrini, A. 1955*a*. Azione della triiodotironina sull'effetto morfocinetico del TSH nel ratto ipofisoprivo. Folia endocrinol. (Pisa), **8**:621–28.

———. 1955*b*. Studi quantitativi sull'apparecchio insulare nel diabete steroideo sperimentale della cavia. Ztschr. Zellforsch., **43**:307–18.

———. 1956. Rapporti tra iperglicemia ed ipertrofia dell'apparato insulare nel diabete steroideo della cavia. Folia endocrinol. (Pisa), **9**:95–102.

Fell, H. G., and Mellanby, E. 1953. Metaplasia produced in cultures of chick ectoderm by high vitamin A. J. Physiol., **119**:470–88.

Ferner, H. R. 1952. Das Inselsystem des Pankreas: Entwicklung, Histobiologie und Pathophysiologie mit besonderer Berücksichtigung des Diabetes Mellitus. Stuttgart: G. Thieme Verlag.

Fields, W. S., Guillemin, R., and Carton, C. A. 1956. Hypothalamic-hypophysial interrelationships. Springfield, Ill.: Charles C Thomas.

Flint, J. M. 1900. The blood-vessels, angiogenesis, organogenesis, reticulum, and histology of the adrenal. Johns Hopkins Hosp. Rep., **9**:153–229.

Frew. J. H. G. 1928. A technique for the cultivation of insect tissues. J. Exper. Biol., **6**:1–11.

Fugo, N. W. 1940. Effects of hypophysectomy in the chick embryo. J. Exper. Zoöl., **85**:271–97.

Fukuda, S. 1944. The hormonal mechanism of larval molting and metamorphosis in the silkworm. J. Fac. Sc. Imp. Univ. Tokyo, Sec. 4, **6**:477–532.

GABE, M. 1952a. Particularités histochimiques de l'organe de Hanström (organe X) et de la glande du sinus chez quelques crustacés décapodes. Compt. rend. Acad. sc., **235**:90–92.

———. 1952b. Sur l'existence d'un cycle sécrétoire dans la glande du sinus (organe pseudofrontal) chez *Oniscus asellus* L. *Ibid.*, pp. 900–902.

———. 1952c. Particularités histologiques de la glande du sinus et de l'organe X (organe de Bellonci) chez *Sphaeroma serratum* Fabr. *Ibid.*, pp. 973–75.

———. 1953. Sur l'existence, chez quelques crustacés malacostracés, d'un organe comparable à la glande de la mue des insectes. *Ibid.*, **237**:1111–13.

GAILLARD, P. J. 1955a. Parathyroid gland tissue and bone in vitro. Parts II–III. Proc. k. nederl. Akad. Wetensch., Ser. C, **58**:279–93 .

———. 1955b. Parathyroid gland tissue and bone in vitro. Exper. Cell Res., Suppl., **3**:154–69.

———. 1957. Parathyroid gland and bone in vitro. Schweiz. med. Wchnschr., **87**:447–50.

GEIGY, R. 1941. Thyroxineinwirkung auf verschieden weit entwickelte Froschlarven. Verhandl. schweiz. Naturforsch. Gesellsch., **121**:161–64.

GESCHWIND, I. I., and LI, C. H. 1955. The tibia test for growth hormone. *In:* The hypophyseal growth hormone, nature and actions, ed. R. W. SMITH, JR., O. H. GAEBLER, and C. N. H. LONG, Part I, chap. 3, pp. 28–53. New York, Toronto, and London: McGraw-Hill Book Co., Inc.

GOLDSCHMIDT, R. 1915. Some experiments on spermatogenesis in vitro. Proc. Nat. Acad. Sc., **1**:220–22.

GONZALES, F. 1956. The functional differentiation of embryonic chick thyroid in roller tube cultures. Exper. Cell Res., **10**:181–87.

GREENWOOD, A. W., and BLYTH, J. S. S. 1935. Variation in plumage responses of Brown Leghorn capons to oestrone. II. Intradermal injection. Proc. Roy. Soc. London, B, **118**:122–32.

GROBSTEIN, C. 1953. Epithelio-mesenchymal specificity in the morphogenesis of mouse sub-mandibular rudiments in vitro. J. Exper. Zoöl., **124**:383–413.

GRUENWALD, P. 1941. The relation of the growing Müllerian duct to the Wolffian duct and its importance for the genesis of malformations. Anat. Rec., **81**: 1–19.

GUDERNATSCH, J. F. 1912. Feeding experiments on tadpoles. I. The influence of specific organs given as food on growth and differentiation. Roux' Arch. Entw.-Mech., **35**:457–83.

GUILLEMIN, R. 1957. Über die hypothalamische Kontrolle der ACTH-Sekretion betrachtet an den Ergebnissen von in vitro-Versuchen. Endokrinologie (Leipzig), **34**:193–201.

GUILLEMIN, R., HEARN, W. R., CHEEK, W. R., and HOUSHOLDER, D. E. 1956. Isolation from the hypothalamus of a substance which stimulates release of ACTH in vitro. Fed. Proc., **15**:84.

GUILLEMIN, R., and ROSENBERG, B. 1955. Humoral hypothalamic control of anterior pituitary: a study with combined tissue cultures. Endocrinology, **57**:599–607.

HAMILTON, H. L. 1940. A study of the physiological properties of melanophores with special reference to their role in feather coloration. Anat. Rec., **78**: 525–47.

HANSTRÖM, G. 1941. Einige Parallelen im Bau und in der Herkunft der inkretorischen Organe der Arthropoden und der Vertebraten. Acta Univ. Lund, N.F., No. 2, **37**:1–19.

HARRIS, G. W. 1955. Neural control of the pituitary gland. London: E. Arnold.

HARTWIG, H. 1940. Metamorphose-Reaktionen auf einen lokalisierten Hormonreiz. Biol. Zentralbl., **60**:473–78.

HAUSBERGER, F. X., and RAMSAY, A. J. 1953. Steroid diabetes in guinea pigs: effects of cortisone administration on blood and urinary glucose, nitrogen excretion, fat deposition, and the islets of Langerhans. Endocrinology, **53**: 423–35.

———. 1955. Steroid diabetes in guinea pigs: effects of hydrocortisone administration on blood and urinary glucose, nitrogen excretion, fat deposition, and the islets of Langerhans. Endocrinology, **56**:533–40.

HELFF, O. M. 1928. Studies on amphibian metamorphosis. III. The influence of the annular tympanic cartilage on the formation of the tympanic membrane. Physiol. Zoöl., **1**:463–95.

HERS, H. G. 1957. Le Métabolisme du fructose. Brussels: Éditions Arscia.

HISAW, F. L., VERLARDO, J. T., and GOOLSBY, C. M. 1954. Interaction of estrogens on uterine growth. J. Clin. Endocrinol., **14**:1134–43.

HOHLWEG, W. 1934. Veränderungen des Hypophysenvorderlappens und des Ovariums nach Behandlung mit grossen Dosen von Follikelhormon. Klin. Wchnschr., **13**:92–95.

HOOKER, C. W., and FORBES, T. R. 1947. A bio-assay for minute amounts of progesterone. Endocrinology, **41**:158–69.

HOWARD, K. S., SHEPHERD, R. G., EIGNER, A. N., DAVIES, D. S., and BELL, P. H. 1955. Structure of β-corticotropin: final sequence studies. J. Am. Chem. Soc., **77**:3419–20.

IRWIN, M. R. 1949. Immunological studies in embryology and genetics. Quart. Rev. Biol., **24**:109–23.

JONES, B. M. 1956. Endocrine activity during insect embryogenesis. Function of the ventral head glands in locust embryos (*Locustana pardalina* and *Locusta migratoria*, Orthoptera). J. Exper. Biol., **33**:174–85.

JOST, A. 1946. Recherches sur la différenciation sexuelle de l'embryon de lapin I. Introduction et embryologie génitale normale. Arch. anat. micr. et morphol. expér., **36**:151–200.

———. 1947a. Recherches sur la différenciation sexuelle de l'embryon de lapin. II. Action des androgènes de synthèse sur l'histogenèse génitale. *Ibid.*, pp. 242–70.

———. 1947b. Recherches sur la différenciation sexuelle de l'embryon de lapin. III. Rôle des gonades fœtales dans la différenciation sexuelle somatique. *Ibid.*, pp. 271–315.

———. 1948. Activité androgène du testicule fœtal de rat greffé sur l'adulte castré. Compt. rend. Soc. biol., **142**:196–98.

———. 1950. Sur le contrôle hormonal de la différenciation sexuelle du lapin. Arch. anat. micr. et morphol. expér., **39**:577–607.

———. 1951. Recherches sur la différenciation sexuelle de l'embryon de lapin. IV. Organogenèse sexuelle masculine après décapitation du fœtus. *Ibid.*, **40**:247–81.

———. 1953. Problems of fetal endocrinology: the gonadal and hypophyseal hormones. Rec. Prog. Hormone Res., **8**:379–418.

———. 1957. The secretory activities of fetal endocrine glands and their effect upon target organs. *In:* Josiah Macy, Jr., Foundation Transactions of the Third Conference on Gestation, pp. 129–71. New York, 1956.

JOST, A., and COLONGE, R. A. 1949. Greffé de testicule fœtal de rat sur l'adulte castré et hypophysectomisé. Remarques sur la physiologie du testicule fœtal de rat. Compt. rend. Soc. biol., **143**:140–42.

KALTENBACH, J. C. 1953*a*. Local action of thyroxin on amphibian metamorphosis. I. Local metamorphosis in *Rana pipiens* larvae effected by thyroxin-cholesterol implants. J. Exper. Zoöl., **122**:21–39.

———. 1953*b*. Local action of thyroxin on amphibian metamorphosis. II. Development of the eyelids, nictitating membrane, cornea, and extrinsic ocular muscles in *Rana pipiens* larvae effected by thyroxin-cholesterol implants. *Ibid.*, pp. 41–51.

———. 1953*c*. Local action of thyroxin on amphibian metamorphosis. III. Formation and perforation of the skin window in *Rana pipiens* larvae effected by thyroxincholesterol implants. *Ibid.*, pp. 449–67.

KARLSON, P. 1956. Biochemical studies on insect hormones. Vitamins & Hormones, **14**:228–66.

KEENE, M. F. L., and HEWER, E. E. 1927. Observations on the development of the human suprarenal gland. J. Anat., **61**:302–24.

KELLER, K., and TANDLER, J. 1916. Über das Verhalten der Eihäute bei der Zwillingsträchtigkeit des Rindes. Untersuchungen über die Entstehungsursache der geschlechtlichen Unterentwicklung von weiblichen Zwillingskälbern, welche neben einem männlichen Kalbe zur Entwicklung gelangen. Wien. Tierärztl. Wchnschr., **3**:513–26.

KITCHELL, R. L., and WELLS, L. J. 1952*a*. Functioning of the hypophysis and adrenals in fetal rats: effects of hypophysectomy, adrenalectomy, castration, injected ACTH and implanted sex hormones. Anat. Rec., **112**:561–91.

———. 1952*b*. Reciprocal relation between the hypophysis and adrenals in fetal rats: effects of unilateral adrenalectomy and of implanted cortisone, doca and sex hormones. Endocrinology, **50**:83–93.

KNOWLES, F. G. W., and CARLISLE, D. B. 1956. Endocrine control in the Crustacea. Biol. Rev., **31**:396–473.

KOLLROS, J. J. 1942. Experimental studies on the development of the corneal reflex in Amphibia. I. The onset of the reflex and its relationship to metamorphosis. J. Exper. Zoöl., **89**:37–67.

———. 1943. Experimental studies on the development of the corneal reflex in Amphibia. II. Localized maturation of the reflex mechanism effected by thyroxin-agar implants into the hindbrain. Physiol. Zoöl., **16**:269–79.

———. 1949. Studies of grafted heads of *Rana pipiens*. Anat. Rec., **105**:491.

———. 1956. Thyroxine and temperature thresholds in anuran metamorphosis. *Ibid.*, **125**:624.

KOLLROS, J. J., and KALTENBACH, J. C. 1952. Local metamorphosis of larval skin in *Rana pipiens*. Physiol. Zoöl., **25**:163–70.

KOLLROS, J. J., and McMURRAY, V. M. 1955. The mesencephalic V nucleus in anurans. I. Normal development in *Rana pipiens*. J. Comp. Neurol., **102**: 47–63.

———. 1956. The mesencephalic V nucleus in anurans. II. The influence of thyroid hormone on cell size and cell number. J. Exper. Zoöl., **131**:1–26.

KONIGSBERG, I. R. 1954. The effects of early pituitary removal by "decapitation" on carbohydrate metabolism in the chick embryo. J. Exper. Zoöl., **125**: 151–69.

LANDAUER, W. 1945. Rumplessness of chicken embryos produced by the injection of insulin and other chemicals. J. Exper. Zoöl., **98**:65–77.

———. 1947*a*. Insulin-induced abnormalities of beak, extremities and eyes in chickens. *Ibid.*, **105**:145–72.

———. 1947*b*. Insulin-induced rumplessness of chickens. V. The effect of insulin on the axial skeleton of chicks and adult fowl. *Ibid.*, pp. 317–28.

LANDAUER, W., and BLISS, C. I. 1946. Insulin-induced rumplessness of chickens. III. The relationship of dosage and of developmental stage at time of injection to response. J. Exper. Zoöl., **102**:1–22.

LANDAUER, W., and LANG, E. H. 1946. Insulin-induced rumplessness of chickens. II. Experiments with inactivated and reactivated insulin. J. Exper. Zoöl., **101**:41–50.

LEE, S. VAN DER, and BOOT, L. M. 1955. Spontaneous pseudopregnancy in mice. I. Acta physiol. et pharmacol. neerl., **4**:442–44.

———. 1956. Spontaneous pseudopregnancy in mice. II. *Ibid.*, **5**:213–15.

LEVINE, R., and GOLDSTEIN, M. S. 1955. On the mechanism of action of insulin. Rec. Prog. Hormone Res., **11**:343–80.

LI, C. H., GESCHWIND, I. I., COLE, R. D., RAACKE, I. D., HARRIS, J. I., and DIXON, J. S. 1955. Amino-acid sequence of alpha-corticotropin. Nature, **176**:687–89.

LILLIE, F. R. 1916. The theory of the free-martin. Science, **43**:611–13.

———. 1917. The free-martin: a study of the action of sex hormones in the foetal life of cattle. J. Exper. Zoöl., **23**:371–452.

———. 1929. Embryonic segregation and its role in the life history. Roux' Arch. Entw.-Mech., **118**:499–533.

LOEB, M. J., and SCHNEIDERMAN, H. A. 1956. Prolonged survival of insect tissues *in vitro*. Ann. Entomol. Soc. America, **49**:493–94.

McCULLAGH, E. P., SIRRIDGE, W. T., and McINTOSH, H. W. 1950. Gametogenic failure with high urinary gonadotropin (FSH). J. Clin. Endocrinol., **10**:1533–46.

McLEAN, F. C. 1943. Physiology of bone. Ann. Rev. Physiol., **5**:79–104.

McLEAN, F. C., and HASTINGS, A. B. 1935. Clinical estimation and significance of calcium-ion concentrations in the blood. Am. J. M. Sc., **189**:601–13.

McPHAIL, M. K. 1934. The assay of progestin. J. Physiol., **83**:145–56.

MANN, T. R. R. 1954. The biochemistry of semen. London: Methuen & Co., Ltd.

MANNER, H. W. 1955. The effect of cortisone acetate on the wound healing phase of *Triturus viridescens*. Growth, **19**:169–75.

MARTINOVITCH, P. N. 1955. Infantile rat adrenal transplanted into the anterior eye chamber of adrenalectomized hosts after cultivation in vitro. J. Exper. Zoöl., **129**:99–127.

———. 1956. Explanation and transplantation of various infantile rat endocrine glands. Transplantation Bull., **3**:37–39.

MERWIN, R. M., and ALGIRE, G. H. 1956. The role of graft and host vessels in the vascularization of grafts in normal and neoplastic tissue. J. Nat. Cancer Inst., **17**:23–33.

MOOG, F. 1950. The functional differentiation of the small intestine. I. The accumulation of alkaline phosphomonoesterase in the duodenum of the chick. J. Exper. Zoöl., **115**:109–29.

———. 1951. The functional differentiation of the small intestine. II. The differentiation of alkaline phosphomonoesterase in the duodenum of the mouse. *Ibid.*, **118**:187–207.

———. 1953. The functional differentiation of the small intestine. III. The influence of the pituitary-adrenal system on the differentiation of phosphatase in the duodenum of the suckling mouse. *Ibid.*, **124**:329–46.

MOOG, F., and RICHARDSON, D. 1955. The functional differentiation of the small intestine. IV. The influence of adrenocortical hormones on differentiation and phosphatase synthesis in the duodenum of the chick embryo. J. Exper. Zoöl., **130**:29–55.

MOORE, C. R. 1941. On the role of sex hormones in sex differentiation in the opossum (*Didelphys virginiana*). Physiol. Zoöl., **14**:1–45.

MOORE, C. R., and PRICE, D. 1932. Gonad hormone functions, and the reciprocal influence between gonads and hypophysis with its bearing on the problem of sex hormone antagonism. Am. J. Anat., **50**:13–71.

MOORE, K. L., GRAHAM, M. A., and BARR, M. L. 1953. The detection of chromosomal sex in hermaphrodites from a skin biopsy. Surg., Gynec. & Obst., **96**:641–48.

MOSER, H. 1950. Ein Beitrag zur Analyse der Thyroxinwirkung im Kaulquappenversuch und zur Frage nach dem Zustandekommen des Frühbereitschaft des Metamorphose-Reaktionssystems. Rev. suisse zool., **57** (Suppl. 2):1–144.

MÜHLBOCK, O. 1939. Versuche über die hormonale Beeinflussung der Federfarbe bei rebhuhnfarbigen Leghorn-Hähnen. Acta brev. neerl., **9**:264–66.

———. 1956. Advanced parental age and spontaneous cancer in mice. Experimentia, Suppl. IV, pp. 78–81.

MÜHLBOCK, O., and BOOT, L. M. 1956. La Fonction hormonale d'ovaires, testicules et hypophyses transplantés chez des souches de souris génétiquement pures. Ann. endocrinol., **17**:338–43.

———. 1957. Die hormonale Funktion transplantierter Ovaria und Hypophysen bei genetisch reinen Mäusestämmen. 4. Symp. deutsch. Gesellsch. Endokrinol., pp. 152–62. Berlin: Springer.

NICKERSON, M. 1946. Conditions modifying the expression of silver in the Silver Campine fowl. Physiol. Zoöl., **19**:77–83.

NIE, R. VAN. 1957. Hormone dependence of transplanted ovarian tumors in mice. Thesis, University of Utrecht.

NIE, R. VAN, and MÜHLBOCK, O. 1956. Hormonal influence on the growth of transplanted ovarian tumours. Acta physiol. et pharmacol. neerl., **4**:572–73.

OLSEN, M. W., and MARSDEN, S. J. 1954. Development in unfertilized turkey eggs. J. Exper. Zoöl., **126**:337–47.

OVERTON, J. 1955. Mitotic responses in amphibian epidermis to feeding and grafting. J. Exper. Zoöl., **130**:433–83.

———. 1956. Control of growth in amphibian epidermis. Anat. Rec., **125**:627.

PANNABECKER, R. 1957. An analysis of sex differentiation in the fetal rat by means of organ culture studies. Ph.D. thesis, University of Chicago.

PESETSKY, I., and KOLLROS, J. J. 1956. A comparison of the influence of locally applied thyroxine upon Mauthner's cell and adjacent neurons. Exper. Cell Res., **11**:477–82.

PIEPHO, H. 1939*a*. Raupenhäutungen bereits verpuppter Hautstücke bei der Wachsmotte, *Galleria mellonella* L. Naturwiss., **27**:301–2.

———. 1939*b*. Über den Determinationszustand der Vorpuppenhypodermis bei der Wachsmotte *Galleria mellonella* L. Biol. Zentralbl., **59**:314–26.

PRICE, D. 1957. Influence of hormones on sex differentiation in explanted fetal reproductive tracts. *In:* Josiah Macy, Jr., Foundation Transactions of the Third Conference on Gestation, pp. 173–186. New York, 1956.

PRICE, D., and PANNABECKER, R. 1956. Organ culture studies of foetal rat reproductive tracts. *In:* Ageing in transient tissues: Ciba Foundation Colloquia on Ageing, 2:3–13. Boston: Little, Brown & Co.

PUCKETT, W. O. 1940. Some effects of crystalline sex hormones on the differentiation of the gonads of an undifferentiated race of *Rana catesbiana* tadpoles. J. Exper. Zoöl., 84:39–51.

PUMPHREY, R. J. 1955. Opening remarks. *In:* The comparative endocrinology of vertebrates. Part I. The comparative physiology of reproduction and the effects of sex hormones in vertebrates, ed. I. C. JONES and P. ECKSTEIN, pp. 1–2. ("Memoirs of the Society for Endocrinology," No. 4.) Cambridge: Cambridge University Press.

RAWSON, R. W., and MONEY, W. L. 1949. Physiologic reactions of the thyroid stimulating hormone. Rec. Prog. Hormone Res., 4:397–428.

RAYNAUD, A., and FRILLEY, M. 1947. Destruction du cerveau des embryos de souris au treizième jour de la gestation, par irradiation au moyen des rayons X. Compt. rend. Soc. biol., 141:658–62.

ROE, J. H., and KUETHER, C. A. 1943. The determination of ascorbic acid in whole blood and urine through the 2,4-dinitrophenylhydrazine derivative of dehydroascorbic acid. J. Biol. Chem., 147:399–407.

RYSSEL, T. G. VAN, NIE, R. VAN, MÜHLBOCK, O., and BRUYN, W. M. DE. 1954. Sarcomatoide transformatie van overgeënte carcinomen. 4d Jaarboek van Kankeronderzoek in Nederland, pp. 17–32.

SAFFRAN, M., and SCHALLY, A. V. 1955. In vitro bioassay of corticotropin: modification and statistical treatment. Endocrinology, 56:523–32.

SAFFRAN, M., SCHALLY, A. V., and BENFEY, B. G. 1955. Stimulation of the release of corticotropin from the adenohypophysis by a neurohypophysial factor. Endocrinology, 57:439–44.

SANGER, F., SMITH, L. F., and KITAI, R. 1954. The disulphide bridges of insulin. Biochem. J., 58:vi–vii.

SANGER, F., and THOMPSON, E. O. P. 1953a. The amino-acid sequence in the glycyl chain of insulin. 1. The identification of lower peptides from partial hydrolysates. Biochem. J., 53:353–66.

———. 1953b. The amino-acid sequence in the glycyl chain of insulin. 2. The investigation of peptides from enzymic hydrolysates. *Ibid.*, pp. 366–74.

SANGER, F., and TUPPY, H. 1951a. The amino-acid sequence in the phenylalanyl chain of insulin. 1. The identification of lower peptides from partial hydrolysates. Biochem. J., 49:463–81.

———. 1951b. The amino-acid sequence in the phenylalanyl chain of insulin. 2. The investigation of peptides from enzymic hydrolysates. *Ibid.*, pp. 481–90.

SAUER, F. C. 1935a. Mitosis in the neural tube. J. Comp. Neurol., 62:377–405.

———. 1935b. The cellular structure of the neural tube. *Ibid.*, 63:13–23.

SCHARRER, B. 1952. Neurosecretion. XI. The effects of nerve section on the intercerebralis-cardiacum-allatum system of the insect *Leucophaea maderae*. Biol. Bull., 102:261–72.

SCHMIDT, E. L., and WILLIAMS, C. M. 1953. Physiology of insect diapause. V. Assay of the growth and differentiation hormone of Lepidoptera by the method of tissue culture. Biol. Bull., **105**:174–87.

SCHMIDT, G.-W. VON, and TONUTTI, E. 1956. Pseudopubertas praecox und unvollständige Pubertas praecox bei einem Leydig-Zell-Tumor des Hodens. Helvet. paediat. acta, **11**:436–54.

SCHNEIDERMAN, H. A. 1957. Onset and termination of insect diapause. *In:* Physiological triggers and discontinuous rate processes, ed. T. H. BULLOCK, pp. 46–59. Washington, D.C.: American Physiological Society.

SEGAL, S. J. 1953. Morphogenesis of the estrogen induced hyperplasia of the adrenals in larval frogs. Anat. Rec., **115**:205–29.

SEGAL, S. J., and NELSON, W. O. 1957. Developmental aspects of human hermaphrodism: the significance of sex chromatin patterns. J. Clin. Endocrinol., **17**:676–92.

SELYE, H. 1949. Textbook of endocrinology. Montreal, Canada: Acta Endocrinologica, Inc.

SHEPHERD, D. M., and WEST, G. B. 1951. Noradrenaline and the suprarenal medulla. Brit. J. Pharmacol., **6**:665–74.

SIMPSON, M. E., ASLING, C. W., and EVANS, H. M. 1950. Some endocrine influences on skeletal growth and differentiation. Yale J. Biol. & Med., **23**:1–27.

SMITH, P. E. 1920. The pigmentary, growth and endocrine disturbances induced in the anuran tadpole by the early ablation of the pars buccalis of the hypophysis. Am. Anat. Mem., No. 11, pp. 1–151.

———. 1933. Increased skeletal effects in A.P. growth-hormone injections by administration of thyroid in hypophysectomized thyro-parathyroidectomized rats. Proc. Soc. Exper. Biol. & Med., **30**:1252–54.

STEFANELLI, A. 1950. Studies on the development of Mauthner's cell. *In:* Genetic neurology, ed. P. WEISS, pp. 161–65. Chicago: University of Chicago Press.

STONE, L. S. 1930. Heteroplastic transplantation of eyes between the larvae of two species of *Amblystoma*. J. Exper. Zoöl., **55**:193–261.

SUN, T. P. 1932. Histo-physiogenesis of the glands of internal secretion—thyroid, adrenal, parathyroid, and thymus—of the chicken embryo. Physiol. Zoöl., **5**:384–96.

SZEGO, C. M., and ROBERTS, S. 1948. Pituitary–adrenal cortical antagonism to estrogenic stimulation of the uterus of the ovariectomized rat. Am. J. Physiol., **152**:131–40.

TAYLOR, A. C. 1943. Development of the innervation pattern in the limb bud of the frog. Anat. Rec., **87**:379–413.

———. 1944. Selectivity of nerve fibers from the dorsal and ventral roots in the development of the frog limb. J. Exper. Zoöl., **96**:159–85.

TAYLOR, A. C., and KOLLROS, J. J. 1946. Stages in the normal development of *Rana pipiens* larvae. Anat. Rec., **94**:7–23.

TEIR, H., LARMO, A., ALHO, A., and BLOMQVIST, K. 1957. Influence of intraperitoneally injected homogenates of the outer orbital gland and the liver on RNA and DNA in these organs in rats. Exper. Cell Res., **13**:147–57.

THIEMER, K. 1953. Zellbild der Langerhansschen Inseln beim Alloxan-Diabetes der hypophysektomierten Ratte und nach Zufuhr von Somatotropin bei normalen Ratten. Endokrinologie (Leipzig), **30**:176–84.

TÖRNBLOM, M. 1949. On the functional relationship between the pituitary gland and the parathyroids. Acta endocrinol., Suppl., **4**:1–76.

TONUTTI, E. 1953. Experimentelle Untersuchungen zur Pathophysiologie der Nebennierenrinde. Verhandl. deutsch. Gesellsch. Path., **36**:123–58.

———. 1956. Hormone und örtliche Reizbeantwortung. Verhandl. deutsch. Gesellsch. inn. Med., 62. Kong., pp. 177–92.

TONUTTI, E., and FETZER, S. 1956. Über Entwicklung und Differenzierung der glandotrop gesteuerten inkretorischen Gewebe beim Menschen. 3. Symp. Deutsch. Gesellsch. Endokrinol., pp. 1–12. Berlin: Springer.

UOTILA, U. U. 1940. The early embryological development of the fetal and permanent adrenal cortex in man. Anat. Rec., **76**:183–203.

VENZKE, W. G. 1943. Endocrine gland weights of chick embryos. Growth, **7**: 265–71.

VOGEL, N. W. 1957. Free tissue cholesterol and growth in chick embryos hypophysectomized by "decapitation." Anat. Rec., **127**:382.

WANG, H. 1943. The morphogenetic functions of the epidermal and dermal components of the papilla in feather regeneration. Physiol. Zoöl., **16**:325–50.

———. 1948. Modulation of tract specificity by estrogenic hormone in experimentally produced feather-chimaerae of Brown Leghorn capons. J. Exper. Zoöl., **109**:451–501.

WATTERSON, R. L., VENEZIANO, P., and BARTHA, A. 1956. Absence of a true germinal zone in neural tubes of young chick embryos as demonstrated by the colchicine technique. Anat. Rec., **124**:379.

WEISS, P. (ed.). 1950. Genetic neurology: problems of the development, growth, and regeneration of the nervous system and of its functions. Chicago: University of Chicago Press.

———. 1955. Specificity in growth control. *In:* Biological specificity and growth, ed. E. G. BUTLER, chap. x, pp. 195–206. Princeton, N.J.: Princeton University Press.

WEISS, P., and FERRIS, W. 1954a. Electronmicrograms of larval amphibian epidermis. Exper. Cell Res., **6**:546–49.

———. 1954b. Electron-microscopic study of the texture of the basement membrane of larval amphibian skin. Proc. Nat. Acad. Sc., **40**:528–40.

———. 1954c. Electron microscopy of the basement membrane of amphibian skin. Excerpta med., **8**:390.

———. 1954d. Electronmicroscopic studies of the amphibian basement lamella. Anat. Rec., **118**:438–39.

WEISS, P., and JAMES, R. 1954. Vitamin A and skin keratinization *in vitro:* experimental dissociation of induction and realization phases in cytodifferentiation. Science, **119**:587.

———. 1955. Skin metaplasia in vitro induced by brief exposure to vitamin A. Exper. Cell Res., Suppl., **3**:381–94.

WEISS, P., and KAVANAU, J. L. 1957. A model of growth and growth control in mathematical terms. J. Gen. Physiol., **41**:1–47.

WEISS, P., and OVERTON, J. H. 1954. Relation between cell growth and mitosis. Excerpta med., **8**:424.

WEISS, P., and ROSSETTI, F. 1951. Growth responses of opposite sign among different neuron types exposed to thyroid hormone. Proc. Nat. Acad. Sc., **37**: 540–56.

WELLS, L. J. 1950. Hormones and sexual differentiation in placental mammals. Arch. anat. micr. et morphol. expér., **39**:499–514.

———. 1957. Effect of fetal endocrines on fetal growth. *In:* Josiah Macy, Jr.,

Foundation Transactions of the Third Conference on Gestation, pp. 187–227. New York, 1956.

WELLS, L. J., and FRALICK, R. L. 1951. Production of androgen by the testes of fetal rats. Am. J. Anat., **89**:63–107.

WICKS, A. E., and SEGAL, S. J. 1956. Time and dose relationships in estriol-estradiol interaction. Proc. Soc. Exper. Biol. & Med., **93**:270–73.

WIGGLESWORTH, V. B. 1934. The physiology of ecdysis in *Rhodnius prolixus* (Hemiptera). II. Factors controlling moulting and "metamorphosis." Quart. J. Micr. Sc., **77**:191–222.

———. 1954. The physiology of insect metamorphosis. Cambridge: Cambridge University Press.

WILKINS, L., and CARA, J. 1954. Further studies on the treatment of congenital adrenal hyperplasia with cortisone. V. Effects of cortisone therapy on testicular development. J. Clin. Endocrinol., **14**:287–96.

WILLIAMS, C. M. 1954. Isolation and identification of the prothoracic gland hormone of insects. Anat. Rec., **120**:743.

———. 1956. The juvenile hormone of insects. Nature, **178**:212–13.

WILLIAMS-ASHMAN, H. G., and BANKS, J. 1954. The ketose reductase of rat liver and accessory sexual organs. Arch. Biochem. & Biophys., **50**:513–15.

WILLIER, B. H. 1921. Structures and homologies of free-martin gonads. J. Exper. Zoöl., **33**:63–127.

———. 1927. The specificity of sex, of organization, and of differentiation of embryonic chick gonads as shown by grafting experiments. *Ibid.*, **46**:409–65.

———. 1930. A study of the origin and differentiation of the suprarenal gland in the chick embryo by chorio-allantoic grafting. Physiol. Zoöl., **3**:201–25.

———. 1939. The embryonic development of sex. *In:* Sex and internal secretions, ed. E. ALLEN, chap. iii, pp. 64–144. Baltimore: Williams & Wilkins Co.

———. 1942. Hormonal control of embryonic differentiation in birds. Cold Spring Harbor Symp. Quant. Biol., **10**:135–44.

———. 1950. Specializations in the response of pigment cells to sex hormones as exemplified in the fowl. Arch. anat. micr. et morphol. expér., **39**:451–66.

———. 1952. Cells, feathers, and colors. Bios, **23**:109–25.

———. 1953. Basic mechanisms in the differentiation of pigment cells. J. Embryol. & Exper. Morphol., **1**:297–99.

———. 1955. Ontogeny of endocrine correlation. *In:* Analysis of development, ed. B. H. WILLIER, P. WEISS, and V. HAMBURGER, Sec. X, pp. 574–619. Philadelphia and London: W. B. Saunders Co.

WILLS, I. A. 1936. The respiratory rate of developing Amphibia with special reference to sex differentiation. J. Exper. Zoöl., **73**:481–510.

WITSCHI, E. 1950. Génétique et physiologie de la différenciation du sexe. Arch. anat. micr. et morphol. expér., **39**:215–46.

———. 1955. Vertebrate gonadotrophins. *In:* The comparative endocrinology of vertebrates. Part I: The comparative physiology of reproduction and the effects of sex hormones in vertebrates, ed. I. C. JONES and P. ECKSTEIN, pp. 149–65. ("Memoirs of the Society for Endocrinology," No. 4.) Cambridge: Cambridge University Press.

———. 1956. Development of vertebrates. Philadelphia: W. B. Saunders Co.

WITSCHI, E., NELSON, W. O., and SEGAL, S. J. 1957. Genetic, developmental and hormonal aspects of gonadal dysgenesis and sex inversion in man. J. Clin. Endocrinol., **17**:737–53.

Wolff, Ét. 1937. L'Hypophyse et la thyroïde jouent-elles un rôle dans le déterminisme expérimental de l'intersexualité chez l'embryo de poulet? Compt. rend. Soc. biol., **126**:1217–18.

Wolff, Ét., and Haffen, K. 1952. Sur l'intersexualité expérimentale des gonades embryonnaires de canard cultivées *in vitro*. Arch. anat. micr. et morphol. expér., **41**:184–207.

Wolff, Ét., and Wolff, Ém. 1951. The effects of castration on bird embryos. J. Exper. Zoöl., **116**:59–97.

Young, F. G. 1953. The growth hormone and diabetes. Rec. Prog. Hormone Res., **8**:471–510.

Zwilling, E. 1948. Association of hypoglycemia with insulin micromelia in chick embryos. J. Exper. Zoöl., **109**:197–214.

PRINTED IN U.S.A.